Practice Book: Units 5–8

NATIONAL GEOGRAPHIC

Reach for Reading

COMMON CORE PROGRAM

NATIONAL GEOGRAPHIC LEARNING | CENGAGE Learning

NATIONAL GEOGRAPHIC LEARNING | CENGAGE Learning

Acknowledgments
Grateful acknowledgment is given to the authors, artists, photographers, museums, publishers, and agents for permission to reprint copyrighted material. Every effort has been made to secure the appropriate permission. If any omissions have been made or if corrections are required, please contact the Publisher.

Cover Design and Art Direction: Visual Asylum

Cover illustration: Joel Sotelo

Illustration Credits: All PM illustrations by National Geographic Learning.

National Geographic Learning | Cengage Learning
1 Lower Ragsdale Drive
Building 1, Suite 200
Monterey, CA 93940

Cengage Learning is a leading provider of customized learning solutions with office locations around the globe, including Singapore, the United Kingdom, Australia, Mexico, Brazil, and Japan. Locate your local office at **www.cengage.com/global**.

Cengage Learning products are represented in Canada by Nelson Education, Ltd.

Visit National Geographic Learning online at **NGL.Cengage.com**
Visit our corporate website a **www.cengage.com**

Printed in the USA.
Sheridan, KY, A CJK Group Company

ISBN: 978-13054-99003 (Practice Book)

ISBN: 978-13056-58707 (Practice Masters)

Printed in the United States of America

21 22 23 24

16 15

Contents

Unit 5: Creature Features

Unit 6: Up in the Air

Unit 7: Then and Now

Unit 8: Get Out the Map!

Name ______________________ Date ____________

Phonics

Words with Soft c

cell phone

face

Circle the word that names the picture. Read and answer the question.

1.

sat
cent
can't

2.

ice
is
ink

3.

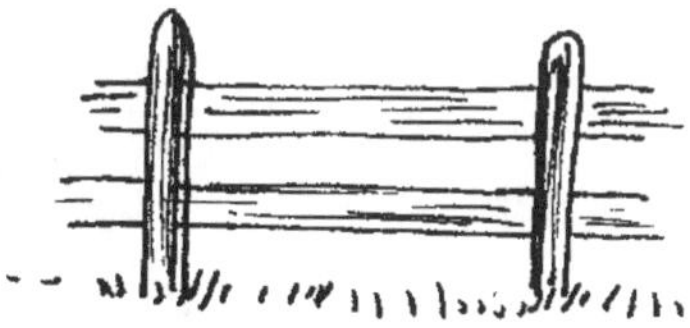

fence
fake
fans

4.

print
price
prize

5.

miles
mice
mink

6.

damp
dash
dance

Read It Together Do mice dance and use cell phones?

Name ______________________ Date ____________

Venn Diagram

Compare and Contrast Animals

Choose two animals. Compare and contrast the animals in the Venn diagram.

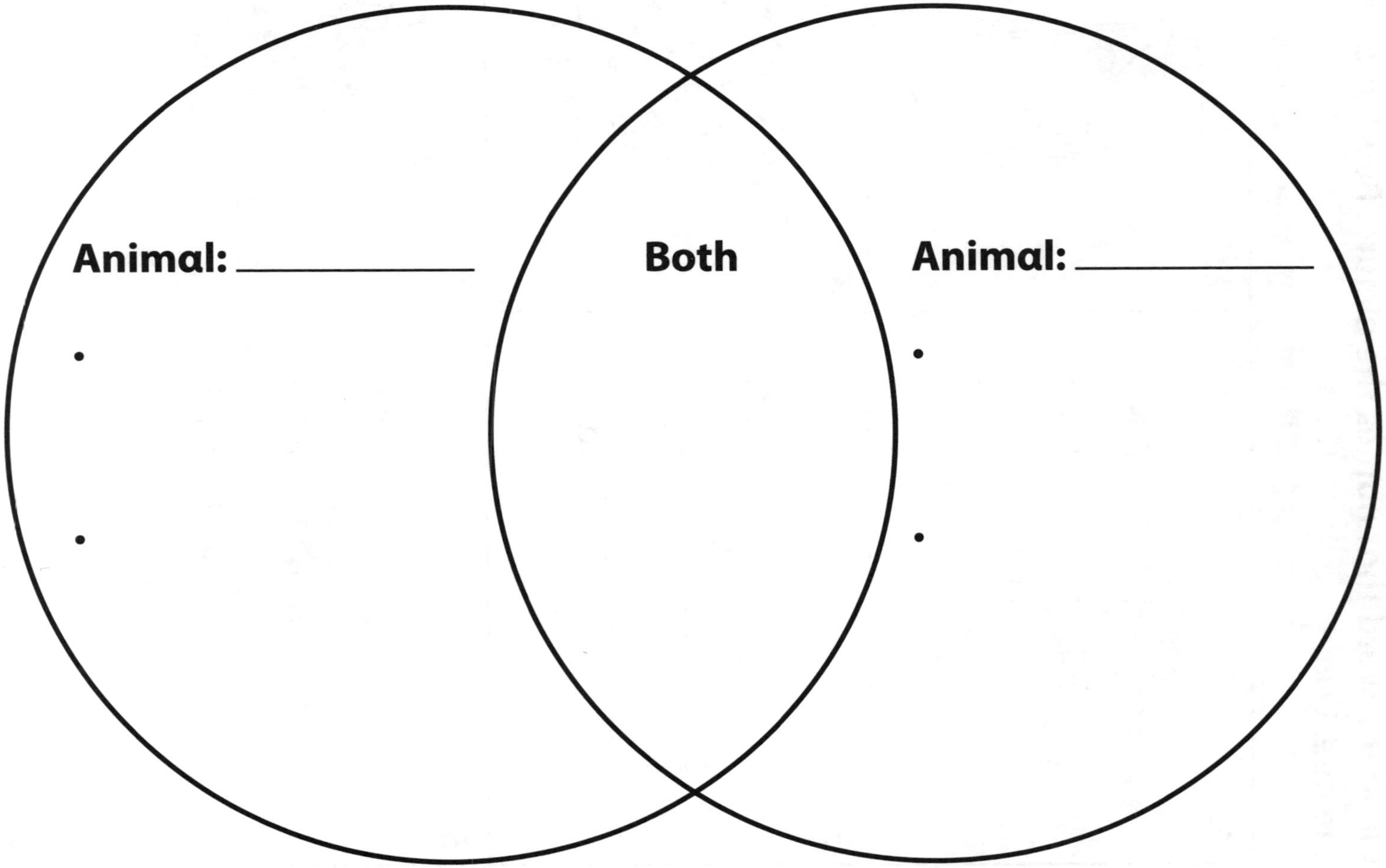

Name ________________________________ Date ______________

Phonics

Words with Soft c

Write the letters to complete the word. Read the sentence.

1.

city

2.

ll

3.

ra

4.

la

5.

nt

6.

pri

Read It Together We'll race from this place to the fence.

Name ______________________ Date ____________

Handwriting

High Frequency Words

Trace each word two times and then write it.

eyes eyes eyes

far far far

small small small

three three three

through through

through

under under under

Spelling & Word Work

Word Cards: Soft *c* and Soft *g*

 ice	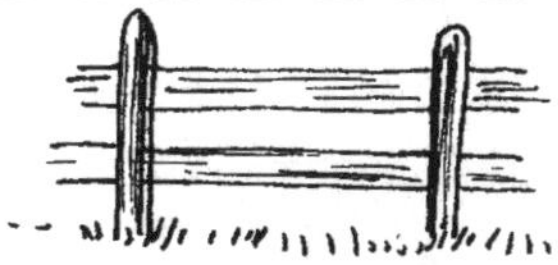 fence	 cage	 giraffe
nice	city	huge	cent
pencil	magic	cellar	gym
face	page	center	gel
mice	spice	age	cell
price	twice	gem	race
space	giant	dance	gentle

Spelling & Word Work

High Frequency Word Cards

because	eyes
carry	far
don't	small
new	three
play	through
sleep	under

Name ______________________ Date ____________

Phonics

Words with Soft g

gem

cage

bridge

Circle the word that names the picture. Read and answer the question.

1.

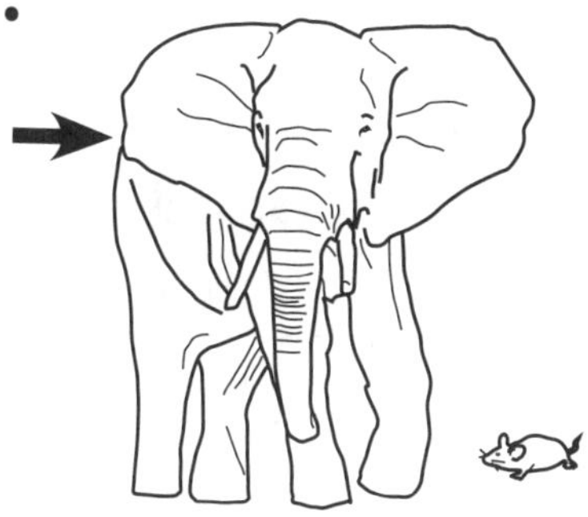

hut

hug

huge

2.

jam

jog

gel

3.

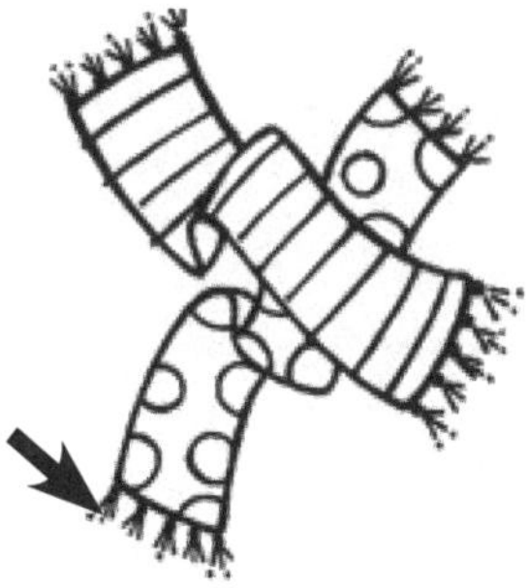

fringe

fling

flag

4.

stack

stag

stage

5.

bang

badge

bag

6.

smudge

smug

smile

Read It Together Would you sing or jog on a huge stage?

Name ____________________ Date ____________

High Frequency Words

The Duck Can Swim

Look at the picture. Write a word from the box to complete each sentence. Read the sentences.

High Frequency Words
eyes
far
small
three
through
under

1. How ____________ will the duck swim?

2. She swims by ____________ frogs.

3. She swims under a ____________ bridge.

4. She swims ____________ some plants.

5. Then she shuts her ____________ to nap!

Name ______________________ Date ____________

Grammar: Possessive Pronouns

Use Possessive Pronouns

Directions:

1. **Make a spinner.**
2. **Play with a partner.**
3. **Take turns spinning the spinner.**
4. **Say a sentence with the pronoun and a word from the word bank.**

bird	lizard	turtle	rabbit	dog	cat

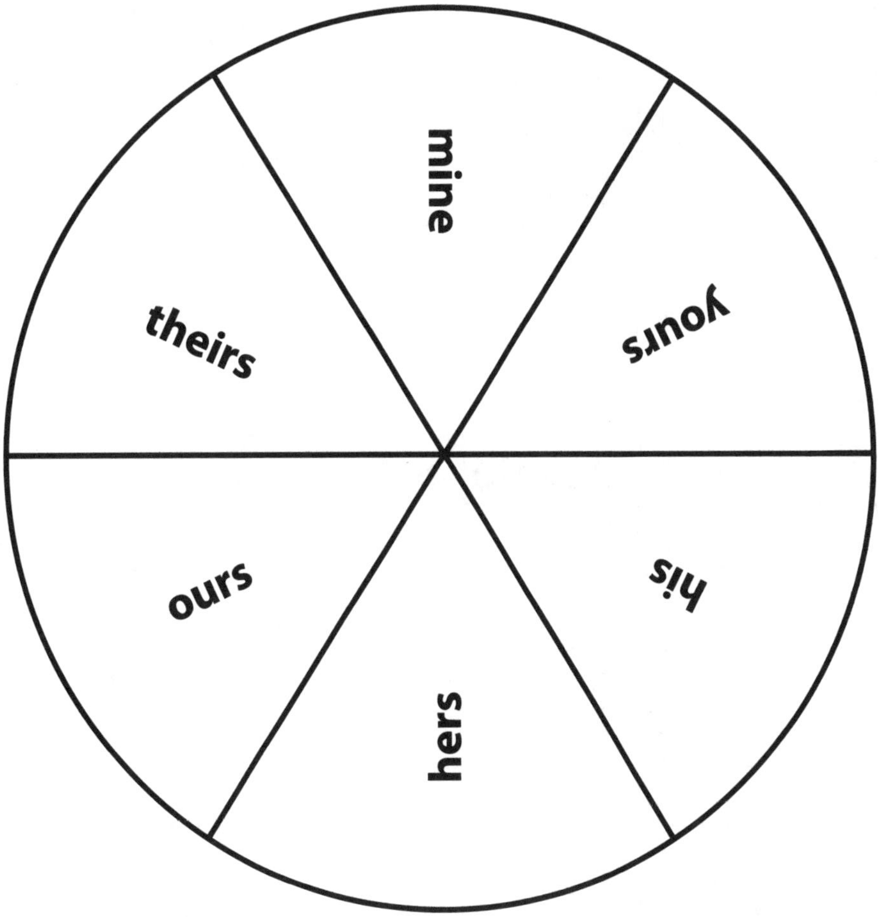

Make a Spinner

1. Put a paper clip in the center of the circle.
2. Hold one end of the paper clip with a pencil.
3. Spin the paper clip around the pencil.

Name ____________________ Date __________

Phonics

Words with Soft g

Write the letters to complete the word. Read the sentence. Tell what else you see.

1. 

page

2. 

ca

3. 

sta

4. 

m

5. 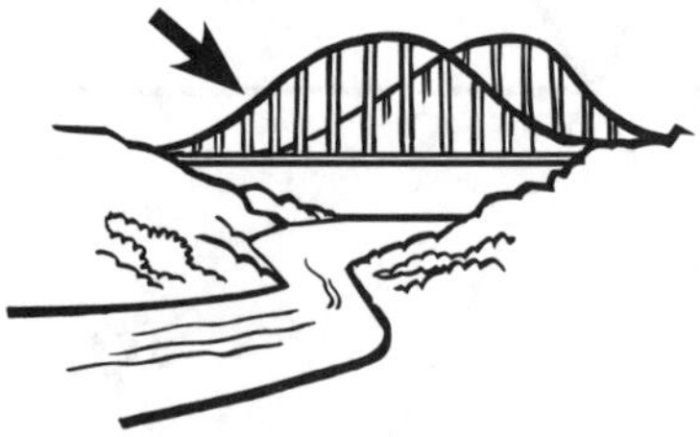

bri

6. 

he

Read It Together I see a hedge and a bridge on this page.

Name ________________________ Date ____________

Grammar & Writing

Write Possessive Pronouns

Read the story. Then choose a word from the box that goes with each sentence.

hers	his	mine	ours	theirs	yours

We have a new book about wild animals. This book is ours.

My favorite animal in the book is the alligator. You also have a favorite animal. Which one is ____________? The book shows a family of flamingos. The baby chicks are ____________. Here is a mother giraffe with her baby. The baby is ____________. Here's a picture of a male monkey. He has a banana. That banana is ____________. I think the baby lizard is really cute. I wish the baby lizard was ____________!

Name ______________________________ Date ______________

Vocabulary

Vocabulary Bingo

1. **Write Key Words.**
2. **Listen to the clues. Place a marker on the Key Word.**
3. **Say "Bingo" when you have four markers in a row.**

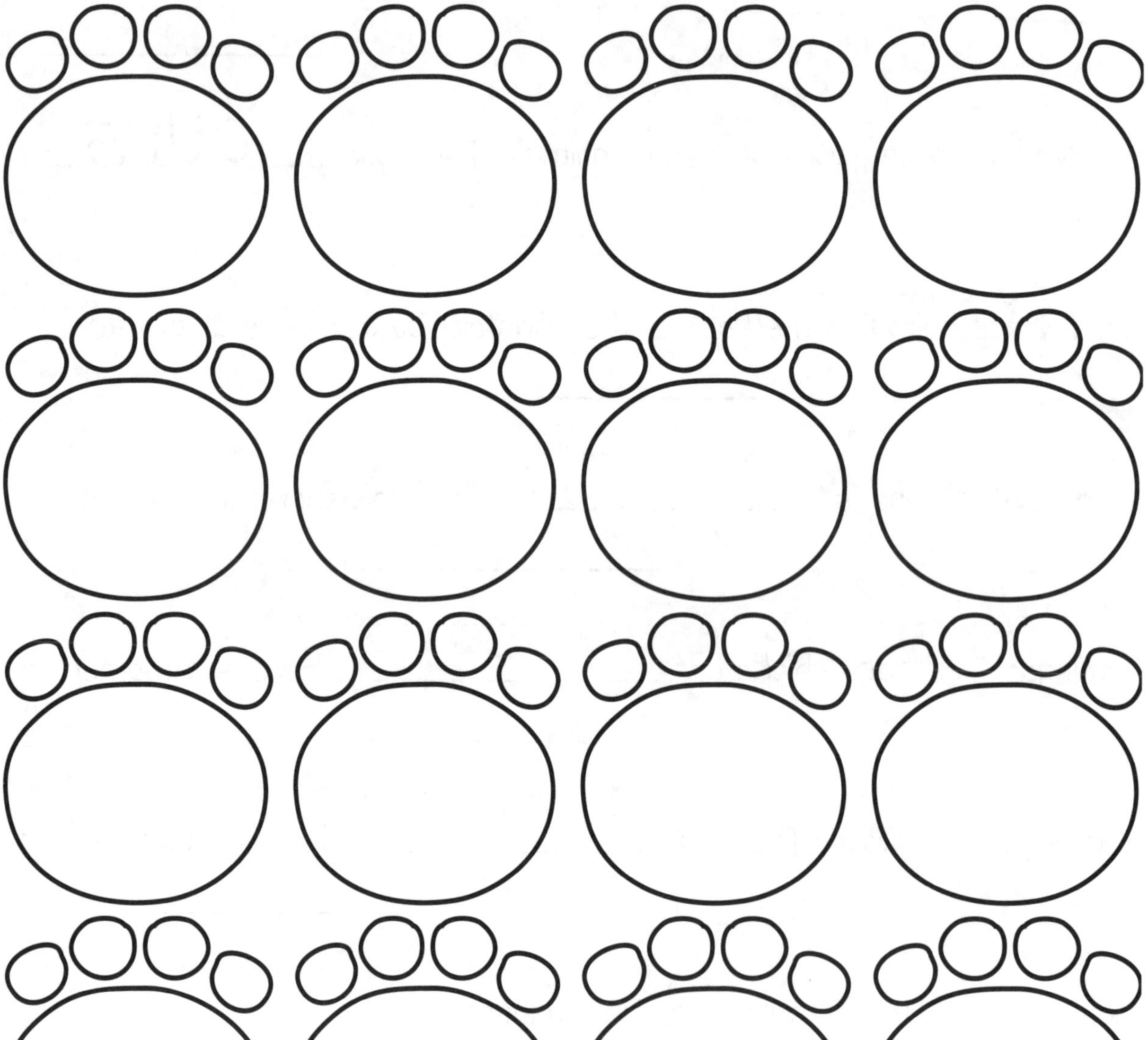

Name ______________________ Date ______________

Venn Diagram

For Pete's Sake

Compare Pete and Pete's friends.

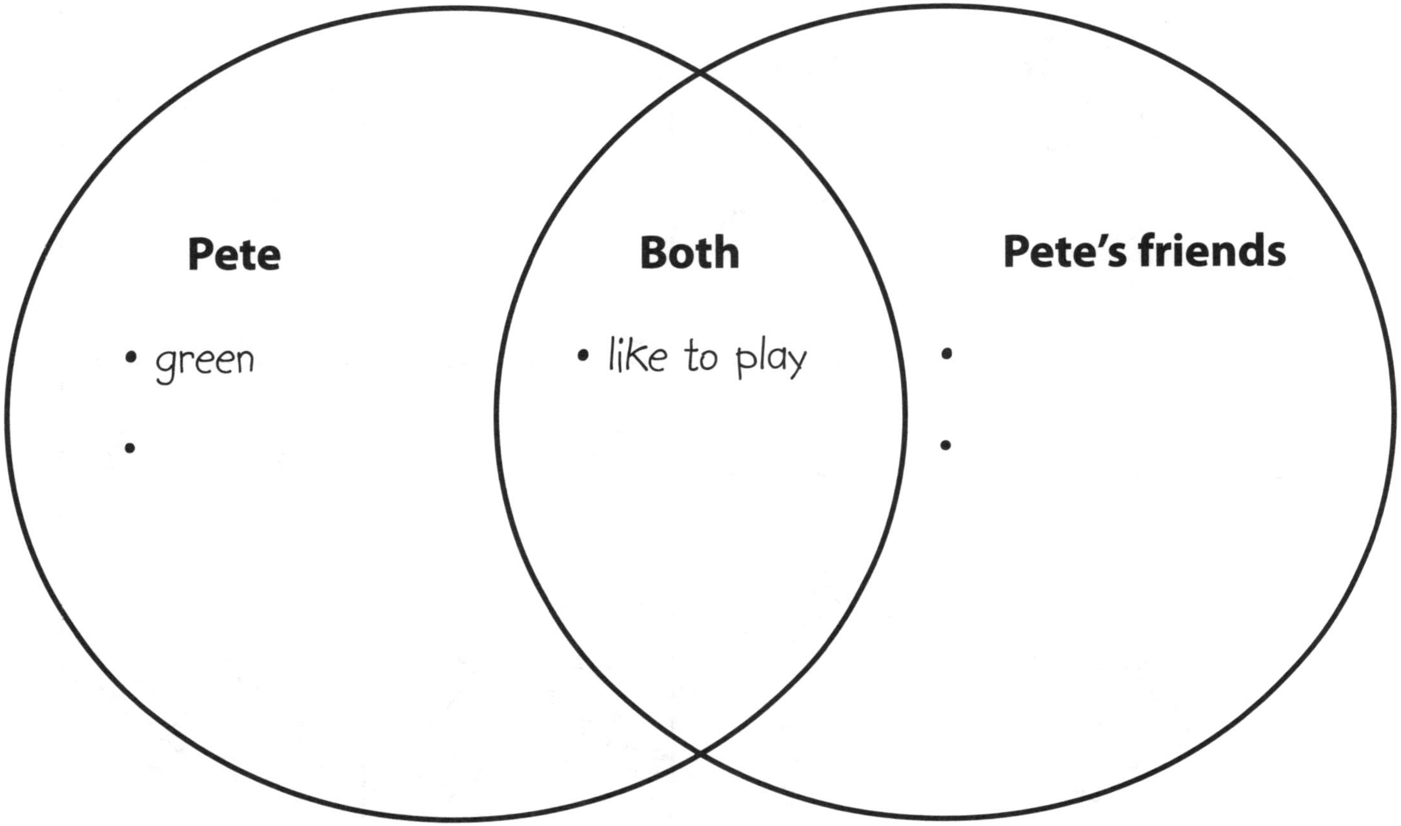

Take turns with a partner. Tell about Pete and Pete's friends. Use your Venn diagram.

Name ______________________ Date ______________

Phonics

Words with -y

fly

bunny

Circle the word that names the picture. Read and answer the question.

1.

post
pen
penny

2.

my
muddy
man

3.

fly
fox
fish

4.

cry
candy
cave

5.

hand
hatch
happy

6.

silly
sky
sea

7.

buggy
by
bone

8.

cake
candy
cry

Read It Together Do you see a buggy or a fly in the sky?

Name ______________________ Date ____________

Phonics

Words with -y

Cut out the cards. Paste each picture under the word that has the same sound for *y*. Use each word in a sentence.

fly

candy

cry

penny

bunny

sky

Name ________________________________ Date ______________

Handwriting

High Frequency Words

Trace each word two times and then write it.

animal animal animal

color color color

group group group

might might might

most most most

move move move

Spelling & Word Work

Word Cards: Words with *-y*

 cry	 fly	 pony	 city
story	family	why	ply
worry	tiny	fry	hurry
body	lady	skinny	sky
spy	try	pretty	spry
puppy	sly	lucky	dry
my	happy	baby	furry

Spelling & Word Work

High Frequency Word Cards

almost	animal
both	color
kind	group
over	might
two	most
was	move

Name ______________________________ Date ______________

Respond and Extend: T-Chart

Compare Genres

Compare a story and a science article.

Animal Fantasy	Science Article
no labels	*has labels*

Tell a partner how a story and a science article are different.

Name ______________________ Date ____________

Phonics

Plurals -s, -es, -ies

Write the plural form of each word. Read and answer the question.

hat	**+ s**	**= hats**
six	**+ es**	**= sixes**
bunny – y	**+ ies**	**= bunnies**

1. 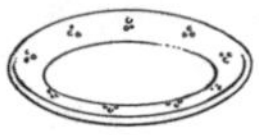 **1 dish**

2 dishes

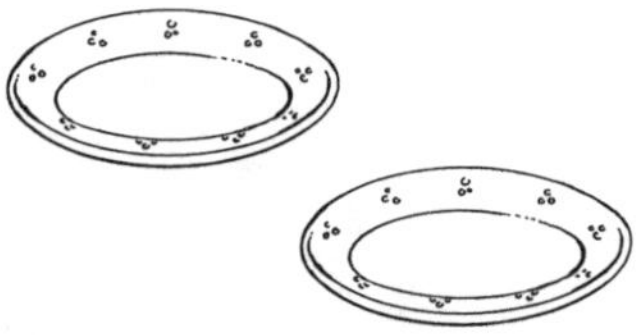

2.  **1 fox**

2 ____________

3.  **1 baby**

2 ____________

4.  **1 cat**

2 ____________

Read It Together Do babies and cats use dishes?

Name ______________________ Date ____________

High Frequency Words

A Red Fox

Look at the picture. Write a word from the box to complete each sentence. Read the sentences.

High Frequency Words
animal
color
group
might
most
move

1. A red fox is a kind of ______________.

2. What ______________ is a red fox?

3. ______________ red foxes are rusty red.

4. Red foxes do not hunt in a ______________.

5. Look! You might see one ______________ through the grass.

Name ______________________ Date ______________

Grammar: Sentences

Expand Sentences

Read each sentence. Then add words to the naming and telling parts of the sentence.

1. Fish eat coral. Colorful fish eat the pointy coral.

2. A fish hides. ______________________

3. A starfish clings. ______________________

4. Birds fly. ______________________

5. The explorers watch. ______________________

Name ______________________ Date __________

Phonics

Plurals -s, -es, -ies

Read the word. Add *-s, -es,* or *-ies* and write the new word on the line. Read the sentences.

ant	**+ s**	**= ants**	
fox	**+ es**	**= foxes**	
puppy – y	**+ ies**	**= puppies**	

finch

1. Two ______________ sit on branches.

bunny

2. Three ______________ hop through the grass.

snake

3. Four ______________ sit on the rocks.

buddy

4. Five ______________ watch the animals.

Name ______________________ Date __________

Grammar & Writing

Write Complete Sentences

Read the paragraph. Write a naming part or a telling part from the box to complete each sentence. Then underline words that tell more about each part.

Naming Parts	Telling Parts
Colorful fish	laps onto the rocks
A large tide pool	scuttle on their spindly legs

At high tide, a wave laps onto the rocks.

Water covers the spiny coral and forms a pool. Shellfish cling to the ledge.

______________________ swim between the plants and

dart under the rocks. Crabs ______________________

______________________ to avoid the water.

______________________ fills the dip in

a rock.

Name ______________________ Date ____________

Grammar: Complete Sentences

Build a Sentence Game

Grammar Rules Complete Sentences

A complete sentence has a naming part and a telling part.

- Start a sentence with a capital letter. A tiger has paws.
- End a sentence with an end mark.

1. Toss a marker onto one of the sentence parts below.

2. Put it together with another sentence part to make a complete sentence.

3. Write the complete sentence on a separate piece of paper.

4. Say the sentence to your partner.

 the monkey	 the elephant
has a tail	 the giraffe
can run	has fur
can climb	 the tiger
 the snake	has a mouth

Name ______________________ Date ____________

Phonics

Words with ai, ay

pail

hay

Circle the word that names the picture. Read the question.

1.

mill

map

mail

2.

ran

rain

run

3.

hat

hay

hen

4.

paint

pen

pan

5.

tap

till

tail

6.

net

nail

nap

7.

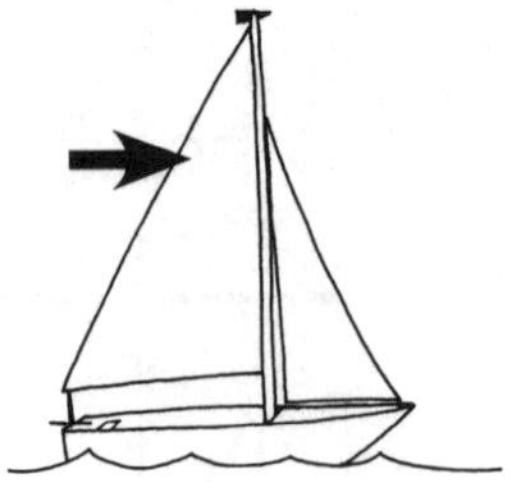

sand

sill

sail

8.

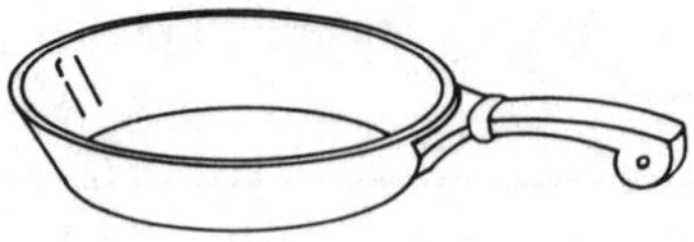

pan

pail

pet

Read It Together Did you say the mail is in the pail?

Name ______________________________ Date ______________

Category Chart

Categorize Movements

Add animals and their movements to the category chart.

Animals	Movement
fish turtle	swim
	fly
	run

Name ____________________ Date ____________

Phonics

Words with ai, ay

Write the letters to complete the word. Read the sentence.

1.

nail

2.

t ___ l

3.

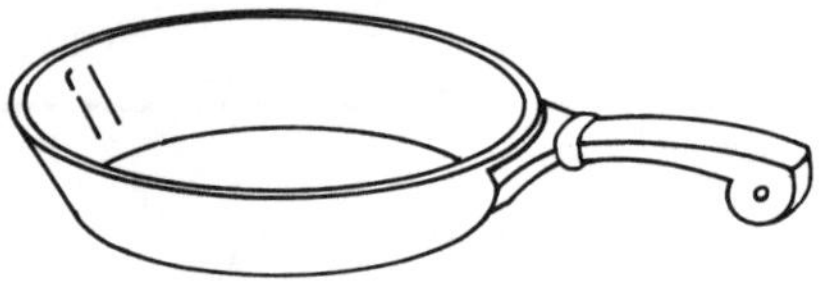

p ___ n

4.

p ___ l

5.

r ___ n

6.

h ___ t

Read It Together I lost my rain hat in the hay.

Name ______________________ Date ____________

Phonics

Blend Words

Circle the word that names the picture. Read and answer the question.

1.

ran rain

2.

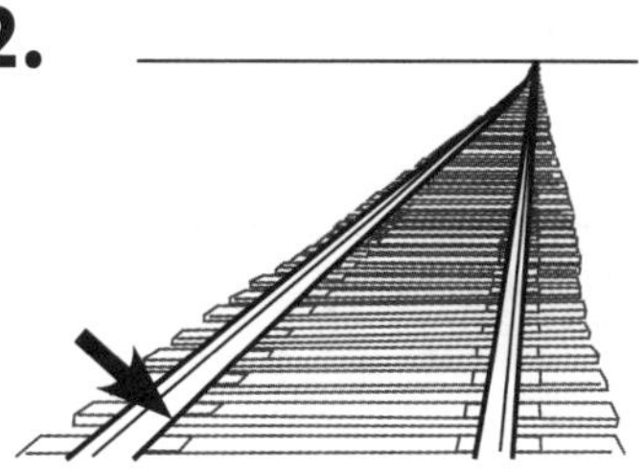

rail rate

3.

wit wait

4.

man main

5.

snail snip

6.

tell tail

7.

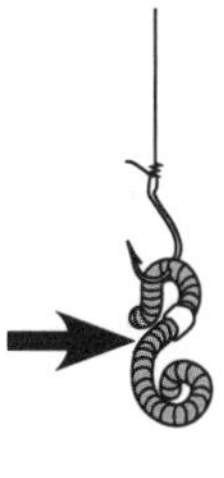

bat bait

8.

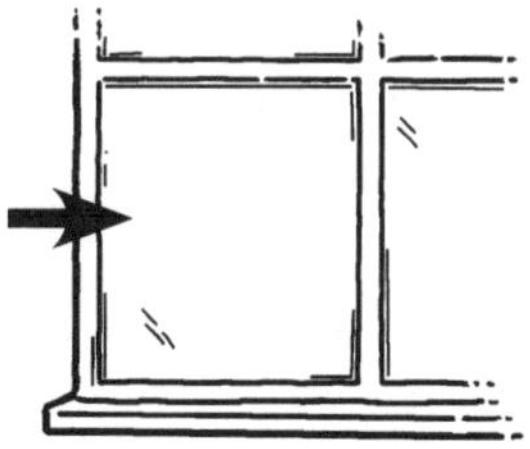

pane pail

9.

pad paid

Read It Together Do you like to wait in the rain?

Name ______________________ Date ____________

Handwriting

High Frequency Words

Trace each word two times and then write it.

funny funny funny

hurt hurt hurt

light light light

mean mean mean

sea sea sea

sound sound sound

Spelling & Word Work

Word Cards: Digraphs *ai, ay*

 train	 ray	 sail	 play
tray	gray	may	pail
hail	mail	stain	day
way	fail	claim	wait
rail	lay	stay	chain
trait	say	trail	bay
clay	quail	bait	hay

Spelling & Word Work

High Frequency Word Cards

always	funny
any	hurt
each	light
every	mean
many	sea
never	sound

Name ______________________ Date ____________

Phonics

Contractions

Write the contraction.
Read the sentence.

I	+	am	=	I'm
he	+	will	=	he'll
you	+	have	=	you've
they	+	are	=	they're

1. We are on the way to see Gramps.

______________ on the way to see Gramps.

2. We have got to take a train there.

______________ got to take a train there.

3. I know it will be a long ride.

I know ______________ be a long ride.

4. I think I am going to take a nap!

I think ______________ going to take a nap!

Name ______________________ Date ______________

High Frequency Words

Yipping and Yapping

Look at the picture. Write a word from the box to complete each sentence. Read the sentences.

High Frequency Words
funny
hurt
light
mean
sea
sound

1. My dog is lost. I hope she isn't ______________ .

2. I look for her while it is ______________ out.

3. These prints ______________ my dog was here!

4. What is that funny yipping ______________ ?

5. It's my dog yapping at the ______________ !

Grammar: Expand Sentences

Word Cards

Mom	Fluffy	Jake
Sarah	Grandpa	Buster
couch	window	garden
door	pond	snake
book	TV	song
call	tell	point
eat	put	turn

Name ______________________ Date ____________

Phonics

Contractions

Write the contraction.
Read the sentence.

I	**+**	**am**	**=**	**I'm**
she	**+**	**will**	**=**	**she'll**
they	**+**	**have**	**=**	**they've**
we	**+**	**are**	**=**	**we're**

1. I am going on a whale watch.

____

______________ going on a whale watch.

2. You have got to come with me!

____

______________ got to come with me!

3. I hope we will see some whales.

____

I hope ______________ see some whales.

4. I know they are out there in the sea!

____

I know ______________ out there in the sea!

Name ______________________ Date ____________

Grammar & Writing

Use End Marks in Sentences

Read each sentence. Then choose an end mark from the box that goes with the sentence. Write it on the blank.

.	!

Dear Mom and Dad,

I have some great news. Just listen to this __.__ We went on a hike _____ We saw a big pond. I looked at the water. I could not believe my eyes _____ What did I see in the water? You had better sit down _____ I saw a huge alligator _____ He looked as big as a car _____ Write back to me _____

Love,
Alex

Name ______________________________ Date ____________

Vocabulary

Rivet

1. Write the first letter of each word.
2. Try to guess the word.
3. Fill in the other letters of the word.

1. ___ ___ ___ ___

2. ___ ___ ___ ___

3. ___ ___ ___ ___ ___ ___ ___ ___

4. ___ ___ ___

5. ___ ___ ___

6. ___ ___ ___ ___ ___

7. ___ ___ ___ ___ ___

8. ___ ___ ___ ___

9. ___ ___ ___ ___

10. ___ ___ ___ ___ ___

11. ___ ___ ___ ___ ___ ___ ___

Name ______________________ Date ____________

Category Chart

Slither, Slide, Hop, and Run

Categorize the animals and their movements in "Slither, Slide, Hop, and Run."

Animals	Movement
birds bats	fly
horses	

Use your category chart to summarize the information in the selection. Work with a partner.

Name ______________________ Date ____________

Phonics

Words with ee, ea, ie

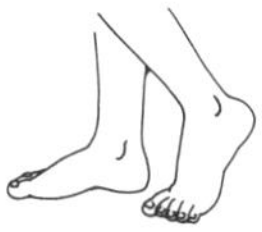
feet

seal

piece

Circle the word that names the picture. Read and answer the question.

1.

bee
by
bay

2.

life
left
leaf

3.

nice
niece
neck

4.

patch
peach
pitch

5.

them
thief
three

6.

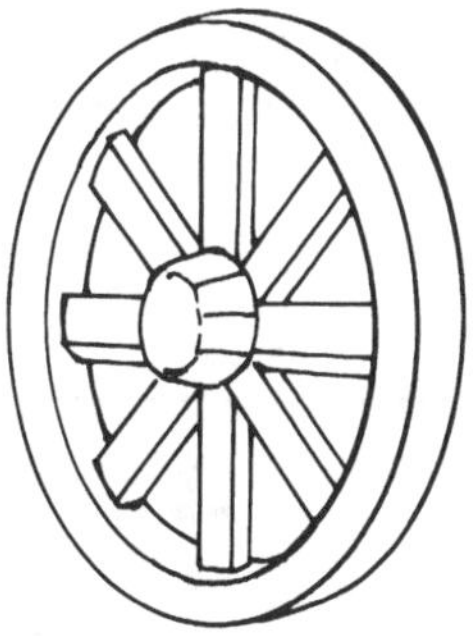

wheel
while
wheat

Read It Together Would a niece eat a peach or a wheel?

Name ____________________ Date ____________

Phonics

Words with ee, ea, ie

Write the letters to complete each word. Read the sentence.

1.

piece

2.

wh l

3.

p ch

4.

s l

5.

f t

6.

n ce

Read It Together A seal swims through a wheel and gets a piece of fish.

Name ____________________ Date ____________

Phonics

Blend Syllables

Circle the word that goes with the picture. Read the sentence.

1.  mail meal	**2.** 16 sailing sixteen
3.  reading raining	**4.**  field feel
5.  playing feeding	**6.** 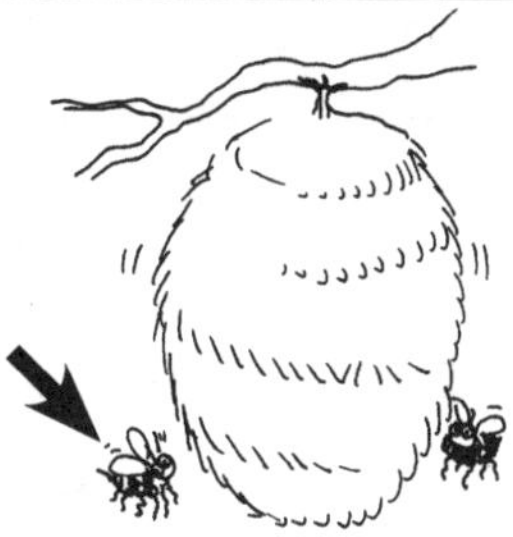 bean bee
7. 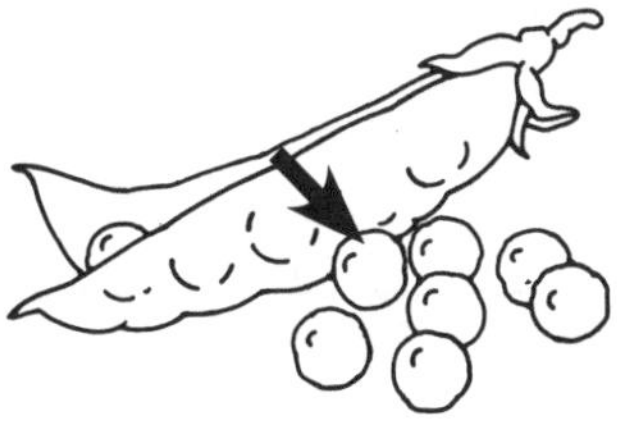 pea play	**8.**  tea team

Read It Together Sixteen kids are reading and playing.

Name ______________________ Date ____________

Handwriting

High Frequency Words

Trace each word two times and then write it.

few few few

food food food

head head head

hold hold hold

into into into

once once once

Word Cards: *ee, ea, ie*

 bee	 leaf	 tree	 field
needle	yield	meat	belief
teapot	chief	feet	eel
week	beat	brief	thief
queen	jeans	beef	niece
clean	leaf	teeth	team

High Frequency Word Cards

four	few
may	food
only	head
other	hold
show	into
some	once

Name ______________________ Date ______________

Venn Diagram

Compare Genres

Compare a fact book and a photo journal.

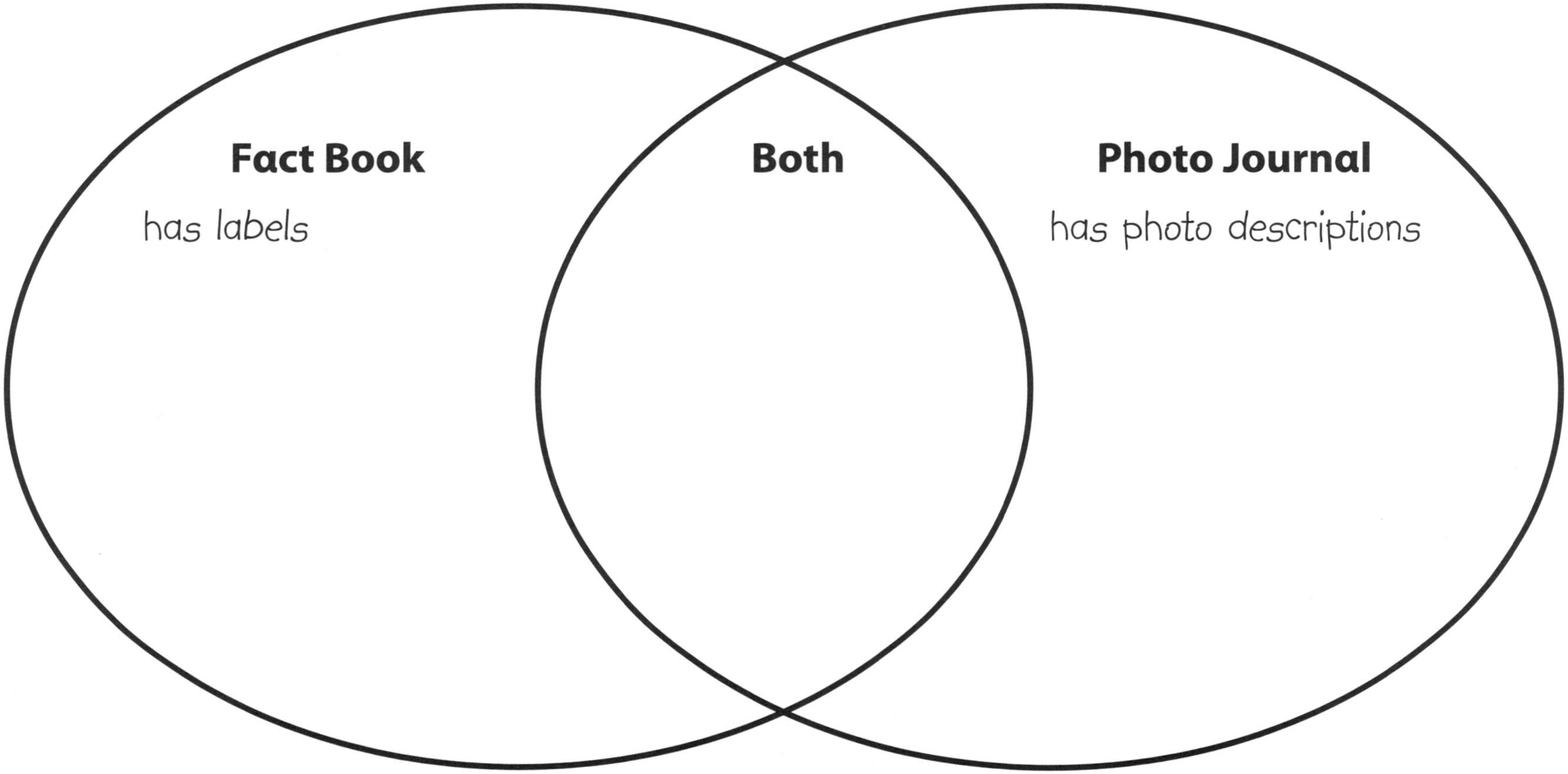

Tell a partner how a fact book and a photo journal are the same. Then tell how they are different.

Name ______________________ Date ____________

Phonics

Ending -ed

Cut out the cards and shuffle them. Then match them and tell how they changed. Act out the words and use them in sentences.

hop	**hopped**
hum	**hummed**
rake	**raked**
skate	**skated**
cry	**cried**
dry	**dried**

Name ______________________ Date ____________

Phonics

Ending -ing

Cut out the cards and shuffle them. Then match them and tell how they changed. Act out the words and use them in sentences.

hop	**hopping**
hum	**humming**
rake	**raking**
skate	**skating**
cry	**crying**
dry	**drying**

Name ____________________ Date ____________

High Frequency Words

Feed the Cat

Look at the picture. Write a word from the box to complete each sentence. Read the sentences.

High Frequency Words
few
food
head
hold
into
once

1. I feed my cat ____________ each day.

2. I put ____________ into his dish.

3. My cat sticks his ____________ into the dish and eats.

4. Then I ____________ him in my lap.

5. I pat him a ____________ times.

Name ______________________ Date ____________

Grammar: Indefinite Pronouns

Match Indefinite Pronouns

Read the words on the left side. Then draw a line that connects each pronoun with the words that make a complete sentence.

1. Anyone	is dangerous.
2. Everything	are now club members.
3. Nothing	then decide to join our nature club.
4. Something	is welcome to our nature club.
5. Two sisters love nature and both	happens and we all become good friends.
6. Many visit and	leave our club after joining.
7. Our teachers are proud of us and several	help us with our club.
8. A few	is fun and easy.

Name ______________________ Date ____________

Phonics

Ending -ed

Read the word. Add *-ed*. Write the new word on the line. Read the sentences.

pop	+ p		+ ed	=	popped
like	– e		+ ed	=	liked
fry	– y	+ i	+ ed	=	fried

flap

1. The seagull ______________ its wings.

glide

2. Then it ______________ up, up, up.

spy

3. I ______________ it way up in the sky.

dip **dive**

4. Then it ______________ and ______________ into the water.

Name ______________________ Date ____________

Phonics

Ending -ing

pop	+ p	+ ing	=	popping
like	– e	+ ing	=	liking
fry		+ ing	=	frying

Read the word. Add *-ing*.
Write the new word.
Read the sentences.

wade

1. Ted is ______________ into the lake.

try

2. Mom is ______________ to teach him to swim.

drip

3. Water is ______________ from him.

grin

4. Ted is ______________ because he can swim!

Name ______________________ Date ______________

Phonics

Endings -s, -es, -ies

Read the word. Add *-s, -es,* or *-ies*.
Write the new word. Read the sentences.

smile		+ s		=	smiles
wax		+ es		=	waxes
dry	– y	+ ies		=	dries

make

1. Kim ______________ eggs for lunch.

mix

2. She ______________ the eggs.

fry

3. She ______________ them in a pan.

help

4. Mom ______________ Kim.

try

5. Then Kim ______________ them. They're good!

Name ______________________ Date ____________

Grammar & Writing

Write Indefinite Pronouns

Read the story. Then choose a word from the box that goes with the sentence and write it on the line.

both	a few	everything
nothing	several	something

Something comes to my bird feeder every night. It ______________ steals all the bird seed. ______________ is left in the morning. ______________ are awake at night to see what it is. But I made a plan. I read some books, and ______________ of them explained my problem. ______________ was ready for the big night. I heard a noise and ran out with a flashlight. I caught two raccoons climbing my bird feeder! ______________ looked right at me. I think they were laughing!

Name ______________________ Date ____________

Grammar: Subject-Verb Agreement

Let's Swim

Grammar Rules **Subject-Verb Agreement**

1. If the subject names one, use *s* at the end of the verb.
2. If the subject names more than one, do not use *s* at the end of the verb.

Choose the verb that goes with the subject. Write the sentence.

1. One fish (swim/swims).

One fish swims.

2. Two fish (swim/swims).

3. A fish (come/comes) here.

4. Many fish (come/comes) here.

Pick a verb from above. Write a new sentence. Read it to a partner.

Name ______________________ Date ____________

Prewrite Graphic Organizer: Main Idea and Details Chart

Main Idea and Details Chart

Main Idea:
Supporting Detail:
Supporting Detail:
Supporting Detail:

Fluency Checklist

- ✓ Did you use more than one kind of sentence?
- ✓ Did you use some short sentences and some longer sentences?
- ✓ Do your sentences flow nicely from one to the next?
- ✓ Does each sentence begin with a capital letter?
- ✓ Does each sentence end with the right end mark?

Name ______________________ Date ______________

Phonics

oa, ow, -old

boat

bow

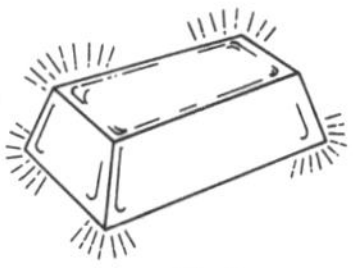
gold

Circle the word that names the picture.

1.  goat gate got	**2.**  box bowl bell
3.  cat coat cake	**4.**  cold cave cot
5.  rod rain road	**6.**  sail soap sock
7.  toad tow told	**8.**  row rope road

Read It Together Does a coat or a bow help if it is cold?

Name ______________________ Date ____________

Cause-and-Effect Chart

Find Cause and Effect

Explain what happens when it rains all day. Write the effects in the cause-and-effect chart.

Cause		Effect
Rain falls all day.	→	Effect
	→	Effect
	→	Effect

Name ______________________ Date __________

Phonics

Words with oa, ow, -old

Circle the word that completes the sentence and write it.

crow **sold**

1. Do you see the big, black ____________ ?

toad **old**

2. It sits in the ____________ oak tree.

toast **scold**

3. I have some ____________ for it to eat.

throw **foam**

4. I ____________ the food.

slow **road**

5. It dives and grabs the food from the ____________ .

Name ______________________ Date ____________

Handwriting

High Frequency Words

Trace each word two times and then write it.

air air air

boy boy boy

different different

different

hurry hurry hurry

soon soon soon

turn turn turn

Spelling & Word Work

Word Cards: *oa, ow, -old*

 coat	 road	 throw	 cold
boat	crow	throat	bowl
old	soap	toad	told
goat	low	bold	row
moat	oak	toast	scold
foam	tow	slow	hold
sold	throw	fold	gold

Spelling & Word Work

High Frequency Word Cards

eyes	air
far	boy
small	different
three	hurry
through	soon
under	turn

Name ______________________ Date ____________

Phonics

Compound Words

Circle the word that names the picture.

1.  raindrop railroad rainbow	**2.**  snowing snowman seashell
3.  watchdog windmill weekday	**4.** 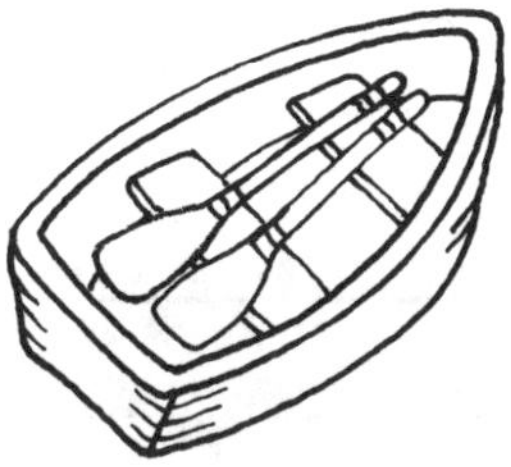 raindrop rowboat roadway
5.  cleanup catfish cupcake	**6.** 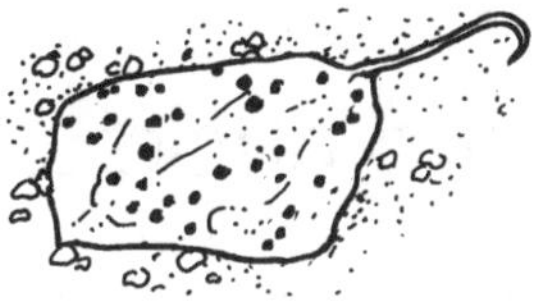 sunscreen stingray snapshot
7.  pancake pinecone pathway	**8.**  peanut pinwheel paintbrush

Read It Together Have you seen pinecones or stingrays?

Name ________________ Date ________

High Frequency Words

Flying Home

Write a word from the box to complete each sentence.

High Frequency Words
air
boy
different
hurry
soon
turn

1. A ________ watches six ducks.
2. How are two ducks ________?
3. They ________ to face east.
4. Then they fly through the ________.
5. They hurry so they will reach their nests ________!

Name ________________________________ Date ______________

Grammar: Compound Sentences

Use Compound Sentences

Play with a partner. The first player circles one word in Box 1 and one word in Box 3. The second player says a compound sentence with the words and uses *and*, *but*, or *or* from Box 2. Play until each player says six sentences.

Box 1	Box 2	Box 3
boy	and	mother
rain	but	wind
cold	or	slow
small	and	tall
light	but	cat
trees	or	houses
duck		fly
girl		father
snow		hot
fast		big
short		dark
dog		bird
ponds		school
bug		eat

Name ______________________ Date ____________

Phonics

Compound Words

Draw a line from the first word to a second word to name the picture. Write the new word.

1.

sail ⋯ fish / boat

sailboat

2.

mail — box / man

____

3.

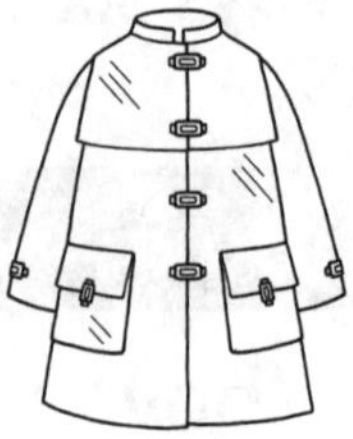

rain — coat / drop

____

3.

snow — bank / flake

____

5.

sea — gull / coast

____

6.

back — pack / seat

____

Read It Together I see seagulls at the seacoast.

Name ____________________ Date ____________

Grammar & Writing

Write *and, but,* or *or*

Read the story. Write a word from the box in each sentence to complete the story.

and	but	or

There's a storm coming, ____and____ I think it might be a big one. We have had some little storms, ____________ nothing as big as this one. We will have to close our windows, ____________ the rain will get in the house. When I was little I was afraid of storms, ____________ I am not afraid now. The thunder is very loud, ____________the big boom scares our dog.

Name ______________________ Date ____________

Vocabulary

Picture It

1. Form pairs. Choose a pair to be the artists and a pair to be the guessers.
2. The artists secretly select a Key Word.
3. The artists draw a picture to show the word's meaning.
4. The guessers guess what Key Word the picture shows.
5. Switch roles.

weather	storm	blow	feel	soft
wind	fast	strong	outside	power

1.	2.
3.	4.

Keeping Score

If the guessers answer correctly, they get 1 point.
The first pair to get 3 points wins!

Name ______________________ Date ____________

Cause-and-Effect Chart

I Face the Wind

Explain the effects of the wind in the story. Use the cause-and-effect chart.

Cause	Effect
The wind blows.	A flag flutters.

Tell a partner facts you learned about the wind in "I Face the Wind." Use your cause-and-effect chart.

Name ______________________ Date ____________

Phonics

Words with ie, igh

pie

light

Circle the word that names the picture.

1.

this

thigh

three

2.

tie

tea

tight

3.

flip

flows

flies

4.

five

fight

fit

5.

nine

night

note

6.

hide

hit

high

Read It Together We need light to see the pie at night.

Name ______________________ Date ____________

Phonics

Words with ie, igh

Complete each word so it names the picture.

1.

light

2.

t

3.

p

4.

b k

5.

p g

6.

n t

Read It Together I tie a flashlight to my bike.

Name ______________________ Date ____________

Handwriting

High Frequency Words

Trace each word two times and then write it.

above above above

again again again

away away away

change change

seven seven seven

sometimes sometimes

Spelling & Word Work

Word Cards: *ie, igh*

 flies	 pie	 night	 flight
dried	pries	right	cries
sight	lie	bright	lies
ties	might	fight	die
high	tonight	sigh	tight
tried	knight	lightning	tied
midnight	cried	tries	spies

Spelling & Word Work

High Frequency Word Cards

animal	above
color	again
group	away
might	change
most	seven
move	sometimes

Name ______________________ Date ____________

Two-Column Chart

Character's Actions

Read Gluscabi's actions. Write the reason for his actions in the chart.

Gluscabi's Actions	Reasons
Gluscabi went to see Wind Eagle.	There was too much wind. Gluscabi couldn't fish.
Gluscabi put Wind Eagle in a hole.	
Gluscabi went to see Wind Eagle again.	
Gluscabi took Wind Eagle out of the hole.	

Choose one of Gluscabi's actions. With a partner, share Gluscabi's reason.

Name ______________________ Date ______________

Phonics

Syllables

Draw a line between syllables. Circle the word that names the picture.

1.

kitten

kidnap

2.

button

basket

3.

cutting

cupcake

4.

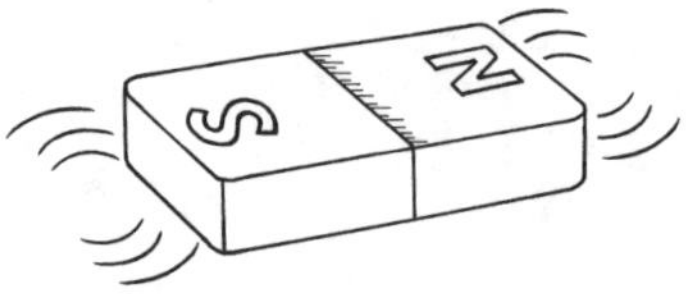

mailbox

magnet

5.

pencil

pigtail

6.

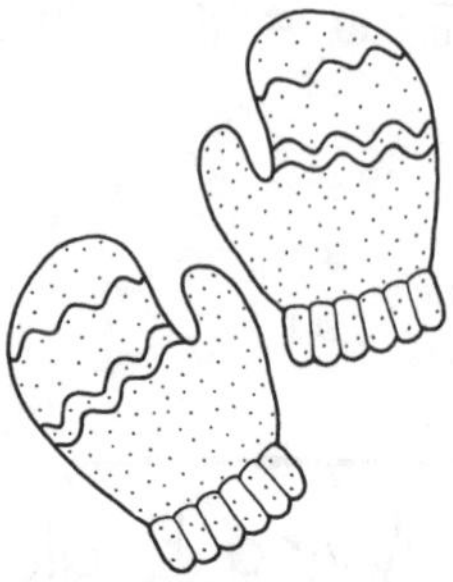

mittens

mealtime

7.

rainbow

rowboat

8.

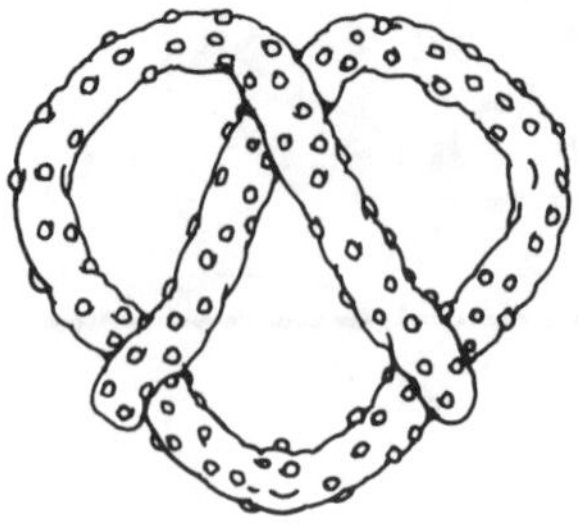

picnic

pretzel

Read It Together I have cupcakes in my basket.

Name ______________________ Date ____________

High Frequency Words

High in the Sky

Write a word from the box to complete each sentence.

High Frequency Words
above
again
away
change
seven
sometimes

1. Sometimes these fly ______________ me in the sky.

2. I look up and see ______________ of them.

3. They ______________ the way they go.

4. They fly one way and then come back ______________.

5. They have strings so they can't fly ______________.
   What are they?

Name ______________________ Date ______________

Grammar: Questions

Build a Question

The first partner puts a marker on a word in each box. The second partner uses the words in a question. The first partner answers the question. Play until each pair has asked and answered four questions.

Box 1			
what	who	where	when
what	who	where	when
what	who	where	when

Box 2			
cloud	coat	mittens	hat
moon	leaves	cricket	swimming pool
bathing suit	eyes	basket	berry

Box 3			
seeds	rain	wind	hair
snow	leaves	birthday	finger
summer	spring	fall	winter

Name ______________________ Date __________

Phonics

Syllables

Draw a line between the syllables. Circle the word that completes eac sentence and write it on the line.

pillow **chipmunk**

1. A ______________ is a little animal.

reptile **invite**

2. It is not a ______________ like a snake.

mammal **traffic**

3. It is a ______________ like a dog or a cat.

cannot **tunnel**

4. It can dig a ______________ to live in.

inside **bedtime**

5. It stays ______________ its home when it is cold out.

Name ______________________ Date ______________

Grammar & Writing

Ask Questions

Write words from the box to complete the sentences in the story.

When	What	Who	Where

Carrie was watching the TV news with her dad. The weather report came on. The weatherman pointed to a map. " Where is it raining today?" Carrie asked.

"It's raining west of here," answered her dad.

" ______________ are you worried about?"

She was worried about their picnic on Saturday.

______________ will it rain here?" asked Carrie.

Just then weatherman pointed to a shining sun on the map. " ______________ does a shining sun mean?" Carrie asked her dad.

"It means the weather will be sunny," her dad said. "

Name ______________________ Date ____________

Grammar: Sentence Types

Use Different Sentence Types

Grammar Rules **Plural Nouns**

1. A statement tells something.
2. A question asks something.
3. An exclamation shows strong feeling.
4. A command tells someone to do something.

You can play outside in the park today. Work with a partner to write about it.

1. Write a statement that tells what you can do in the park.

I can ride my bike.

2. Write a question about the park.

____

3. Write to show how you feel about playing in the park.

____

4. Tell your friend to bring something to the park.

____

Name ______________________ Date ______________

Phonics

oo, ou, ew

spoon

soup

chew

Circle the word that names the picture.

1.  zee zone zoo	**2.**  nose news nice
3.  boot boat bait	**4.**  throw threw three
5.  group grape grew	**6.**  pail pool peel
7.  boo blew bee	**8.** 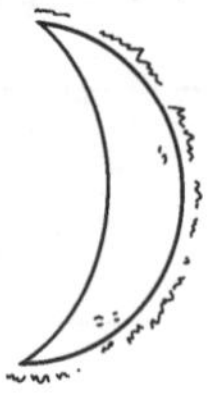 mule main moon

Read It Together I blew on the soup to cool it.

Name ______________________ Date ____________

Classification Chart

Classify Details

Classify activities people do in different kinds of weather.

Cool •	**Cold** •
Warm •	**Hot** •

What We Do in Different Weather

Name ______________________________ Date ______________

Grammar: Expand Sentences

Build Sentences

like	eat	wear	talk
ask	read	saw	run
play	drink	walk	fly
my brother	my sister	my friend	my uncle
my dad and I	her dog	his friend	I
basketball	my parrot	in the rain	shiny red boots
sandwiches	lemonade	yellow	on Saturday
at school	with Mom	on the porch	in the car
when it snows	up in the air	at the park	while I wait
older	little	tall	hairy

Name ______________________ Date ____________

Phonics

Words with oo, ou, ew

Read and trace each word. Write the word that completes each sentence.

roots group grew shoot

1. A little ______________ is growing in my plant pot.

2. It ______________ from a seed that I planted.

3. It has ______________ at the bottom.

4. Do you see this ______________ of buds on it?

5. Soon the ______________ will grow into a big plant.

Name ______________________ Date ____________

Handwriting

High Frequency Words

Trace each word two times and then write it.

been been been

down down down

hard hard hard

now now now

number number number

push push push

Spelling & Word Work

Word Cards: *oo, ou, ew, ue, ui, u_e*

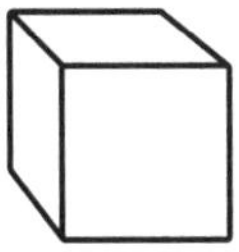 cube	 moon	 fruit	 soup
flute	blue	spoon	cool
root	rule	group	cue
coupon	chew	threw	blew
true	clue	news	boot
few	due	flew	youth
prune	suit	mule	cruise

Spelling & Word Work

High Frequency Word Cards

funny	been
hurt	down
light	hard
mean	now
sea	number
sound	push

Name ______________________________ Date ______________

Phonics

ue, ui, u_e, ew

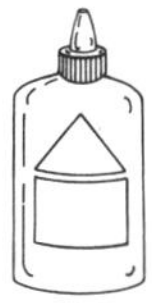
glue

suit

tube

chew

Circle the word that names the picture.

1.

fuel (circled)
few
fold

2.

few
fruit
fry

3.

due
duck
dunes

4.

screw
Sue
scrap

5.

float
flute
flew

6.

stew
sniff
snowsuit

7.

truth
threw
throat

8.

cube
clue
cue

Read It Together Sue and Luke eat stew and fruit for lunch.

Name ______________________ Date ____________

High Frequency Words

Swing Time

Write a word from the box to complete each sentence.

High Frequency Words
been
down
hard
now
number
push

1. I have ______________ pushing Josh on the swing.

2. My push is soft, and then it is ______________ .

3. Josh swings up and then back ______________ .

4. We say a ______________ for every push.

5. We are up to sixteen ______________ !

Name ______________________ Date ____________

Phonics

Words with ue, ui, u_e, ew

Read and trace each word. Write the word that completes each sentence.

few clues tube suit

1. Where is Ruth? I'll give you some ____________.

2. Ruth has her ____________ on so she can swim.

3. She floats in a big ____________.

4. She sees a ____________ fish swim below.

5. What other ____________ can you give for a lake?

Name ______________________________ Date ______________

Phonics

Syllables

Draw a line between syllables. Circle the word that names the picture.

1.

15

flag|pole

feed|back

fif|teen

2.

broken

button

beanbag

3.

penny

puppet

puppy

4.

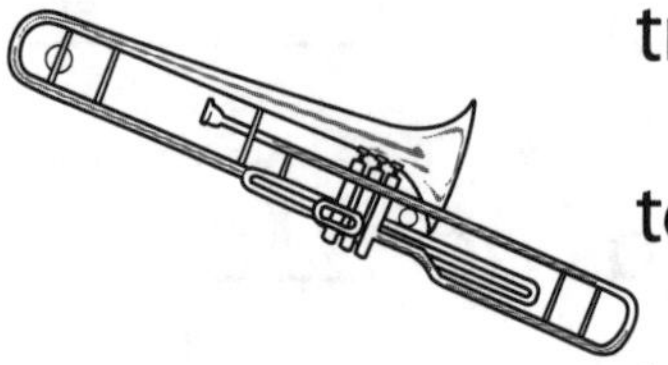

trombone

tennis

traffic

5.

rainbow

raccoon

rabbit

6.

cactus

cupcake

cannot

7.

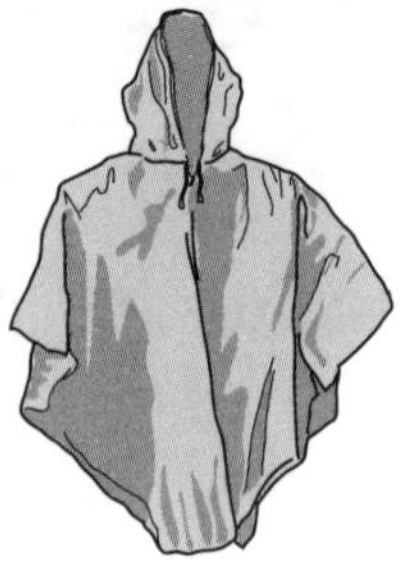

poncho

pillow

public

8.

picnics

pinecones

pancakes

Read It Together Would you eat fifteen pancakes?

Name ______________________ Date ____________

Grammar & Writing

Expand Sentences

Read the letter. Choose words from the box for each sentence.

early	a lot of	around campfires
never	always	because you will get hungry

Here is some advice for your camping trip.

1. Always be prepared for bad weather.

2. Be careful ______________________.

3. Go to bed ____________. Then you will get enough rest.

4. Take snacks ______________________
______________________.

5. ______________________ take silly chances.

Have ______________________ fun!

Love, Grandpa

Name ______________________________ Date ______________

Vocabulary

Rivet

1. **Write the first letter of each word.**
2. **Try to guess the word.**
3. **Fill in the other letters of the word.**

1. ___ ___ ___ ___

2. ___ ___ ___ ___

3. ___ ___ ___

4. ___ ___ ___ ___ ___ ___ ___ ___ ___ ___ ___

5. ___ ___ ___ ___ ___

6. ___ ___ ___ ___ ___ ___

7. ___ ___ ___ ___ ___ ___ ___ ___

8. ___ ___ ___ ___

9. ___ ___ ___ ___ ___

10. ___ ___ ___ ___ ___

11. ___ ___ ___ ___ ___

12. ___ ___ ___ ___

Take turns with a partner. Choose a word. Say it in a sentence.

Name ______________________ Date ____________

Classification Chart

A Year for Kiko

Add details to the classification chart about things Kiko does in different weather.

What Kiko Does in Different Weather

Cool

- plays in grass

Cold

-

Warm

-

Hot

-

Retell "A Year for Kiko" to a partner. Use your chart and illustrations in the story.

Name ________________________ Date ____________

Phonics

au, aw, -alk

auto yawn talk

Circle the word that names the picture.

1.  launch lunch laws	**2.** 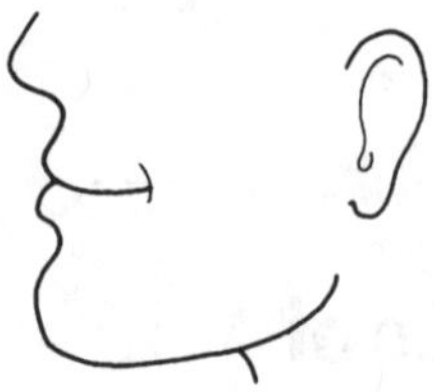 jam jay jaw
3.  dune dawn draw	**4.**  wake whack walk
5.  crawl cause crack	**6.**  fault fawn fast
7.  laundry lawn landing	**8.**  saws sauce sandbox

Read It Together Have you gone for a walk at dawn?

Name ______________________ Date ____________

Phonics

Words with au, aw, -alk

Read and trace each word. Write the word that completes each sentence.

claws hawk haul stalk

1. A ____________ flies high in the sky.

2. Does it ____________ animals while it flies?

3. Now the ____________ swoops down.

4. It grabs a small animal in its ____________ .

5. Then it will ____________ its food away.

Name ______________________ Date ____________

Handwriting

High Frequency Words

Trace each word two times and then write it.

children children

her her her

house house house

school school school

thought thought thought

word word word

Spelling & Word Work

Word Cards: *au, aw, -alk*

 talk	 auto	 claw	 draw
awful	fawn	walk	awed
stalks	thaw	lawn	prawn
balk	haul	because	haunt
pause	August	hawk	cause
straw	awesome	sauce	law
saw	caulk	author	Saul

Spelling & Word Work

High Frequency Word Cards

few	children
food	her
head	house
hold	school
into	thought
once	word

Name ______________________ Date ____________

T-Chart

Compare Genres

Compare a story and an interview.

Realistic Fiction	Interview
has characters	has real people

Use your T-chart to talk about which kind of text you like best. Give reasons.

Name ______________________ Date ____________

Phonics

Words with oo, ea

book

bread

Circle the word that names the picture.

1.

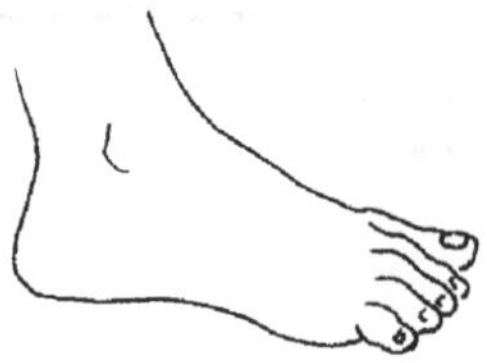

fight
fit
foot

2.

head
hood
hide

3.

read
road
roof

4.

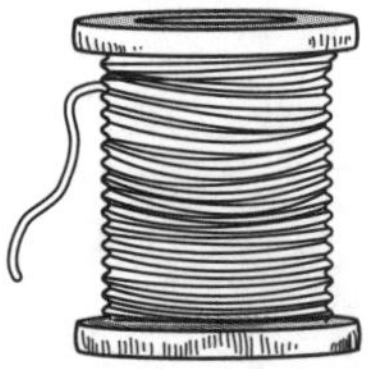

throw
thread
three

5.

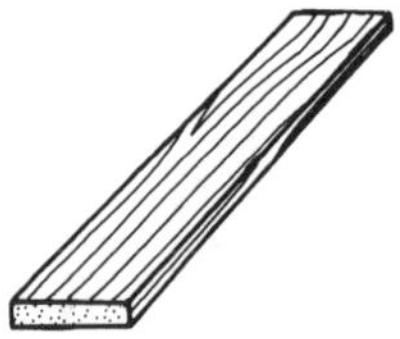

wood
weed
wind

6.

heal
hike
hook

7.

spool
spread
spray

8.

cook
cake
crack

Read It Together The cook spreads jelly on the bread.

Name ______________________ Date ____________

High Frequency Words

I'm Thinking of a Word!

Write a word from the box to complete each sentence.

High Frequency Words
children
her
house
school
thought
word

1. This word means "did think." It is ____________.

2. This names a kind of home. It is ____________.

3. This word means "kids." It is ____________.

4. You use this for a mom. It is ____________.

5. This word is ____________. You go there to read and to do math.

Name ______________________________ Date ______________

Grammar: Questions

Asking Compound Questions

Choose two question words from Box 1 for your partner. Your partner will then choose two words from Box 2 and ask a compound question using all four words. Combine sentences using *and*, *but*, or *or*. Cross out each word in Box 2 as you use it. Reuse the words in Box 1.

Box 1
how
why
who
when
where
what

Box 2				
live	friend	pet	cat	dog
like	snow	rain	wind	here
there	ever	mom	dad	brother
sister	sad	happy	fast	slow
ice	fall	hurt	late	early
dinner	lunch	home	school	room
class	read	watch	go	come
water	apple	bread	walk	run
play	game	write	book	TV
movie	winter	fall	summer	spring
chair	bed	draw	paint	door
window	out	in	to	from
with	for	on	always	never
sometimes		often		

Name ______________________ Date ____________

Phonics

Words with <u>oo</u>, <u>ea</u>

Complete each word so it names the picture.

1.

hood

2.

sw__ter

3.

f__ther

4.

c__kie

5.

h__f

6.

br__kfast

Read It Together Do you eat bread at breakfast?

Name ______________________ Date ____________

Phonics

Syllables

Draw a line between the syllables. Circle the word that names each picture.

1.

notebook

nineteen

noontime

2.

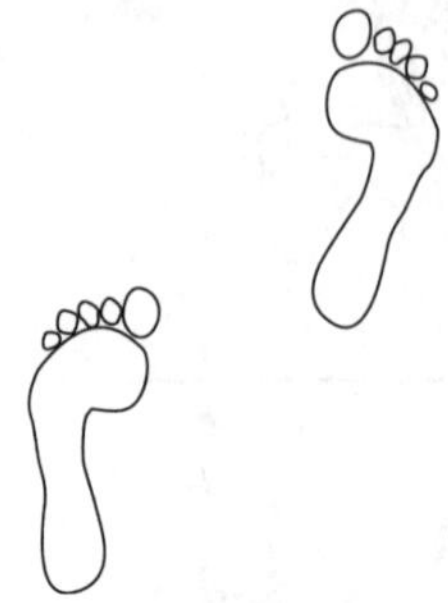

footrest

footpath

footprint

3.

houseboat

headlight

headband

4.

classroom

clambake

clubhouse

5.

bookcase

bedroom

beanstalk

6.

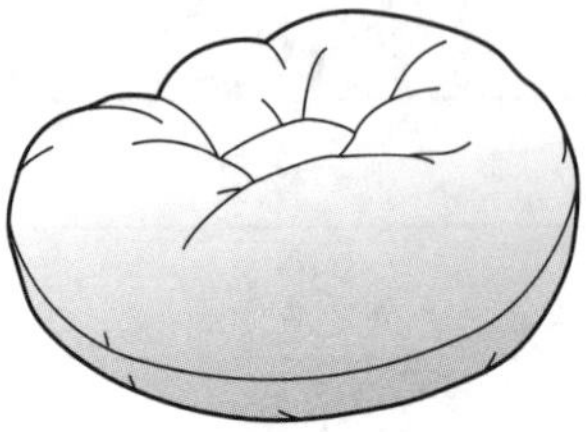

bookshop

beanbag

beehive

7.

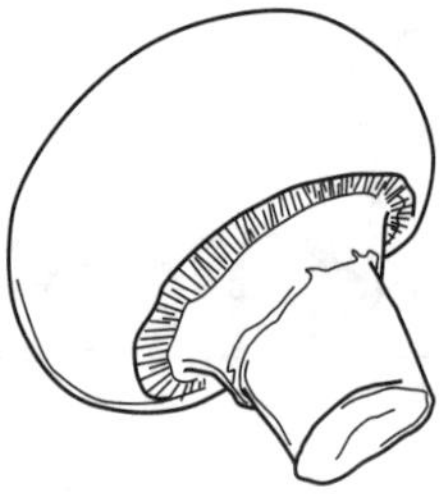

mushroom

mealtime

mailbox

8.

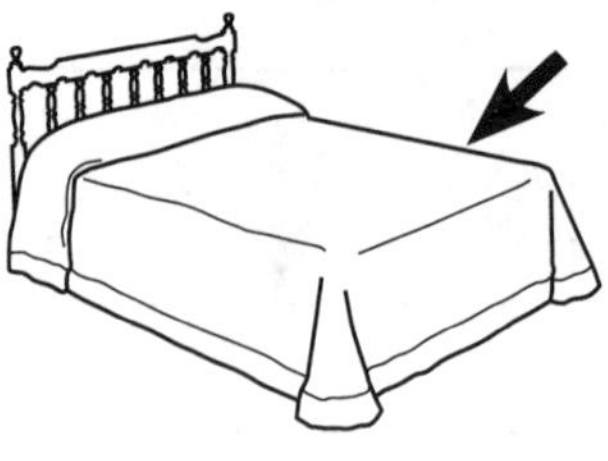

beanpole

bedspread

breakfast

Read It Together Do you see bookcases in a classroom?

Name ______________________ Date ____________

Grammar & Writing

Using Questions

Choose a word from the box to correctly complete each sentence.

how	why	when	where	who	what

TV Reporter: Why are you here today?

Dr. Danger: I am here because your town has storms.

TV Reporter: ______________ did you know our town has storms? ______________ did you get here?

Dr. Danger: I saw storms on the Internet. I came today.

TV Reporter: ______________ is on your team?

Dr. Danger: We have scientists and researchers.

TV Reporter: ______________ will you go next? ______________ do you hope to find there?

Dr. Danger: I will go to Mexico to find storms.

Name ____________________ Date ____________

Grammar: Ask Questions

Question Words

Grammar Rules Ask Questions

Question Words	Information
Who	person
Where	place
What	thing or action
Why	reason
When	time
How	way something is done

Circle the question word. Then write the type of information it gives. Choose from words in the Information column above.

1. When are we going ice skating? time

2. Where is the park? ____________

3. What should I bring? ____________

4. Who is going? ____________

Write a new question about the park. Use a question word. Have a partner say the type of information it gives.

Name ______________________ Date ____________

Prewrite: Cause-and-Effects Chart

Weather Cause-and-Effects Chart

Cause		Effects
	→	
	→	
	→	
	→	

Ideas Checklist

✓ Does the paragraph tell why something happens?
✓ Does the paragraph have interesting ideas?
✓ Did the writer give details?
✓ Do the details help readers picture the weather?

Name ______________________________ Date ______________

Phonics

Words with ar

star

Circle the word that names each picture.

1.  yawn yam yarn	**2.**  farm fame fawn
3. 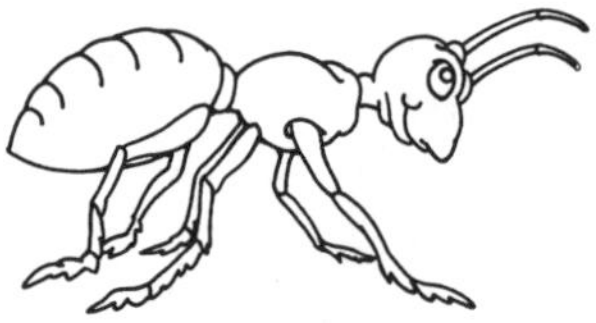 art ant at	**4.**  arm am aim
5.  back bake bark	**6.**  lack lark lake
7.  park pack pace	**8.**  shake shark shack

Read It Together Do you see a barn or a shark at a farm?

Name ______________________________ Date ____________

Main Idea and Details Diagram

Identify Main Idea and Details

Complete the diagram. Write different ways people communicate.

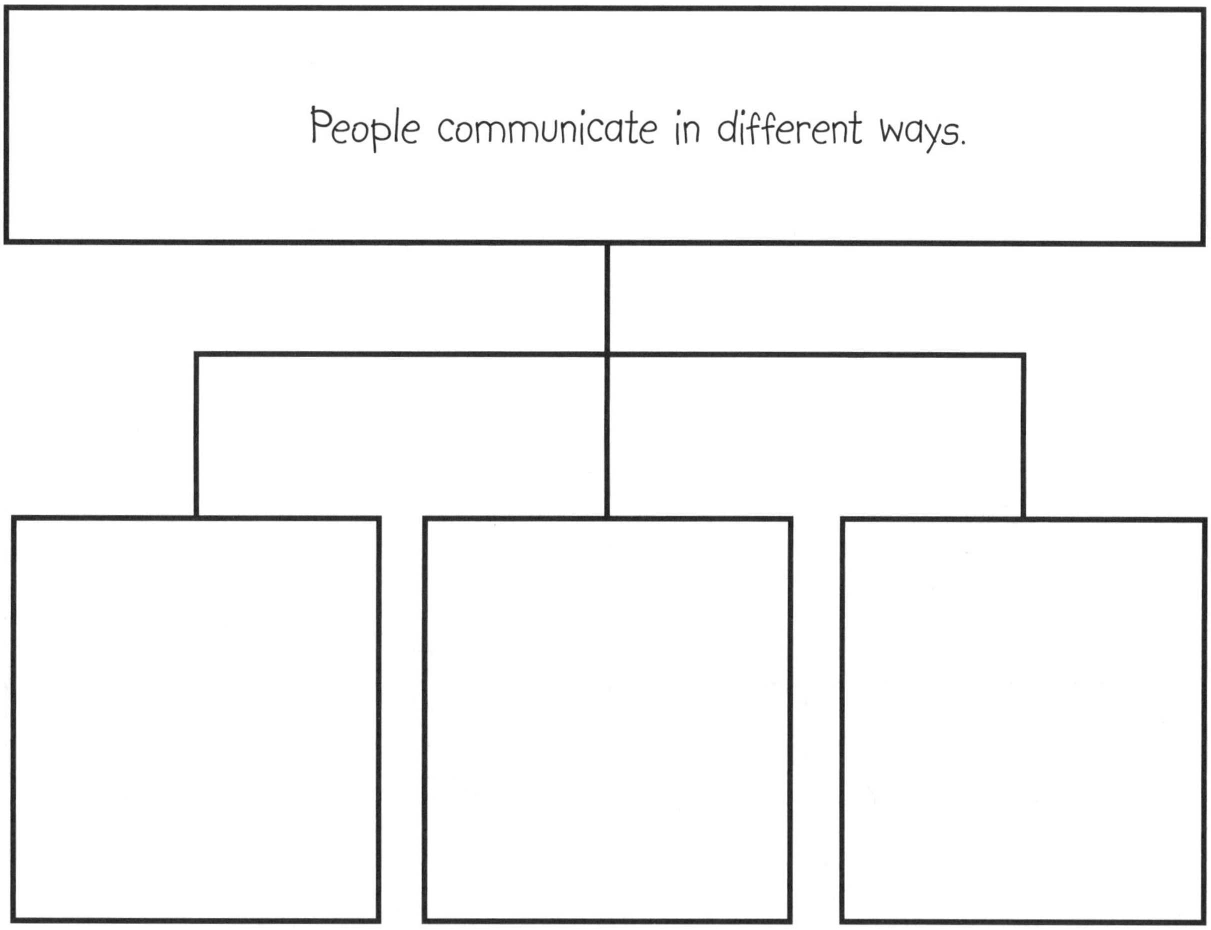

Name ______________________ Date ____________

Phonics

Words with ar

Complete the word so it names the picture.

1. 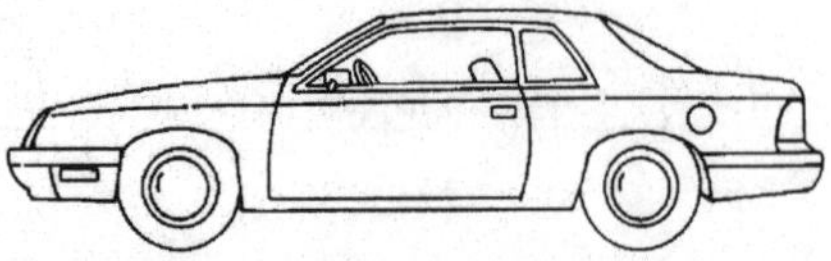 car	2. 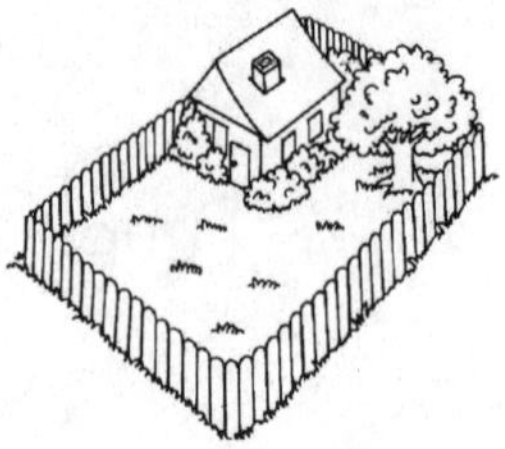 y__d
3. 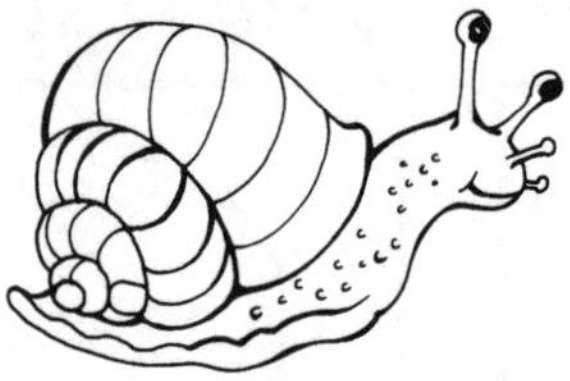 sn__l	4. 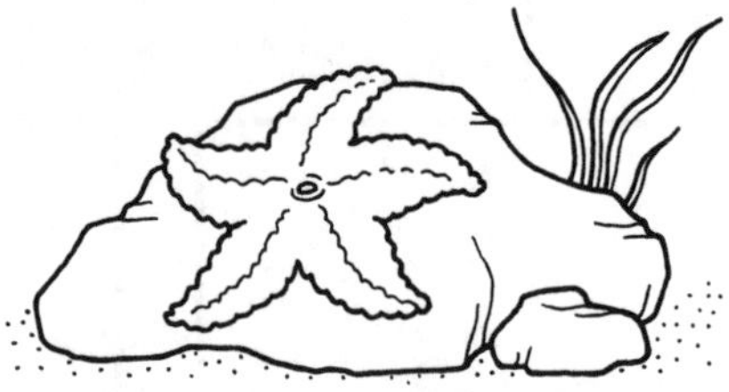 st__fish
5.  g__den	6.  m__ket

Read It Together Would you see a starfish in your yard?

Name ______________________ Date __________

Handwriting

High Frequency Words

Trace each word two times and then write it.

before before before

could could could

people people people

today today today

warm warm warm

were were were

Word Cards: *ar*

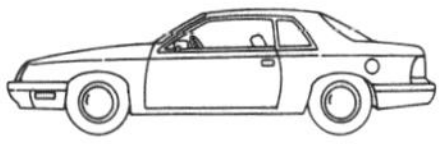 car	 shark	 jar	 arm
charm	far	dart	chart
star	dark	bar	stark
park	farm	yarn	cart
tart	lark	hard	bark
barn	yard	tar	part
card	harm	start	mark

Spelling & Word Work

High Frequency Word Cards

air	before
boy	could
different	people
hurry	today
soon	warm
turn	were

Name ______________________ Date ____________

Phonics

kn, wr, gn, mb

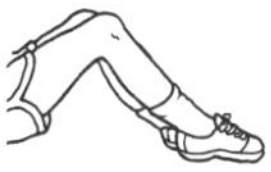

knee

wreath

gnu

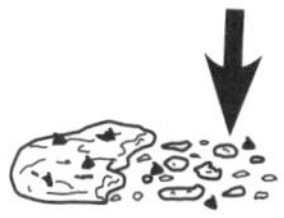

crumb

Circle the word that names the picture.

1.

chat
gnat
rat

2.

lab
lake
lamb

3.

knit
kit
gnash

4.

write
knight
white

5.

soon
sight
sign

6.

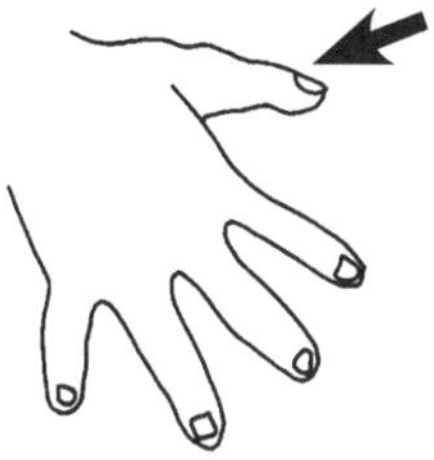

tub
thumb
thud

7.

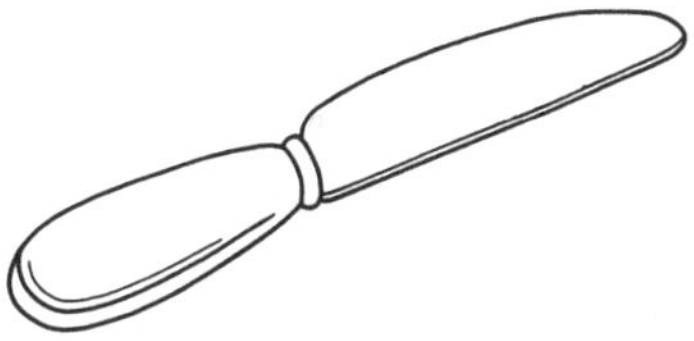

knife
wife
reef

8.

twist
nest
wrist

Read It Together

This is my wrist. This is my thumb. This is my knee.

Name ______________________________ Date ______________

High Frequency Words

Warm Days

Write a word from the box to complete each sentence.

High Frequency Words
before
could
people
today
warm
were

1. What do you do on a ______________ day?

2. Some ______________ go to the beach.

3. We ______________ there on Sunday.

4. It is too cold to go ______________ .

5. We'll wait for a hot day ______________ we go again!

Name ______________________ Date ____________

Grammar: Regular Past Tense

Write Past-Tense Verbs

Grammar Rules Regular Past Tense

To make a verb tell about the past:

- Add -**ed** to the end of many regular verbs, like **look** → **looked**.
- If a one-syllable verb ends in a vowel and consonant, double the final consonant and add -**ed**, like **stop** → **stopped**.
- If a verb ends in **y** with a consonant before it, change the **y** to **i** and add -**ed**, like **hurry** → **hurried**.

Work with a partner. Read a sentence. Add *-ed* to the bold word. Check for spelling changes. Write the new word. Say the sentence.

1. Last week, I hurried to the mailbox. **hurry**
2. I ______________ you a letter. **mail**
3. You ______________ right away! **reply**
4. I was so happy, I ______________ up and down. **hop**
5. Today, I ______________ a welcome sign **print**

Name ______________________ Date ____________

Phonics

Words with kn, wr, gn, mb

Complete each word so it names the picture.

1.

sign

2.

cli

3.

ot

4.

en

5.

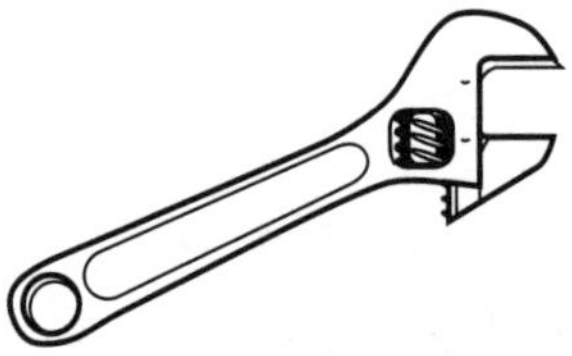

ench

6.

ight

Read It Together Can you tie a knot in a rope?

Name ______________________ Date __________

Grammar & Writing

Write in the Past Tense

Read the story. Then write a word from the box that best completes each sentence.

hugged	looked	walked	pulled	grinned	carried

My family went on a plane trip. We walked to the gate. I got on the plane and went to my seat by the window. When the plane took off, I __________ down at the roads below. Years ago, horses __________ wagons on those roads. People __________ things everywhere in wagons. Soon, the plane ride was over. Mom __________ me and said, "Isn't this a great way to travel?" I __________. It sure is!

Name ______________________________ Date ______________

Vocabulary

Around the World

1. **The traveler stands behind a challenger.**
2. **Listen to the clue. Find the Key Word and say it.**
3. **The first to answer correctly travels to the next student on the right. The first traveler to go all around the circle wins.**

KEY WORDS

news	computer	message	past	future

CLUES

- We can send a ________ with e-mail.
- I have some ________ to share about our school.
- In the ________, I will be an adult.
- My mom reads e-books on her ________.
- In the ________, I was a baby.

Name ______________________ Date ______________

Main Idea and Details Diagram

Communication Then and Now

Complete the diagram below. Write about how communication has changed.

Communication has changed.

Stories		Messages		News	
Then	**Now**	**Then**	**Now**	**Then**	**Now**
pictures	words				

Use your diagram to retell the article to a partner.

Name ______________________________ Date ______________

Phonics

Words with or, ore

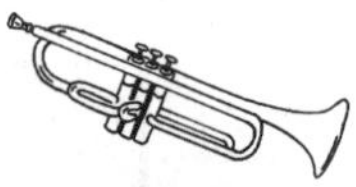

horn

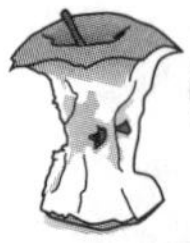

core

Circle the word that names each picture.

1.

con
corn
car

2.

shoot
shot
short

3.

star
store
stay

4.

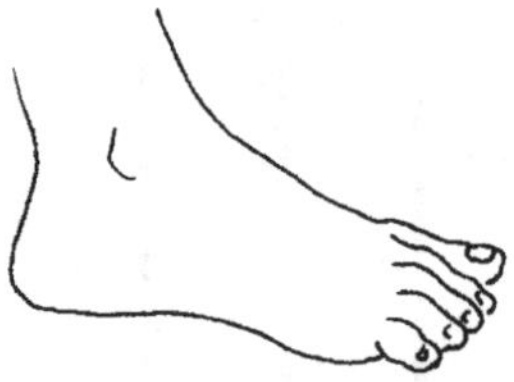

fat
fort
foot

5.

more
mart
moo

6.

sprint
sport
spot

7.

tore
tar
tea

8.

hose
horse
hoops

Read It Together We can get more corn at the store.

Name ______________________ Date ____________

Phonics

Words with or, ore

Complete each word so it names the picture.

1.

fork

2.

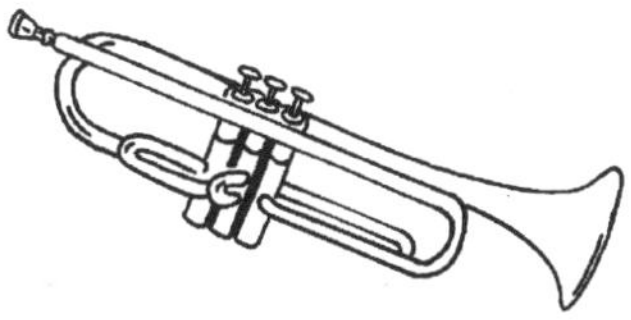

h ___ n

3.

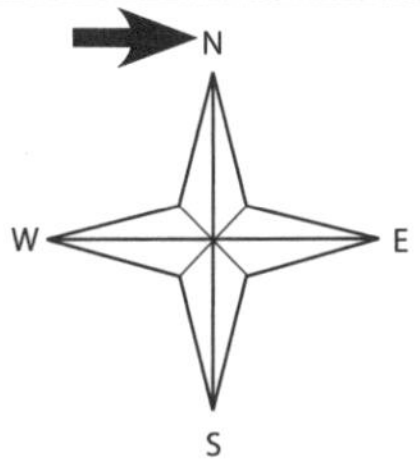

n ___ th

4.

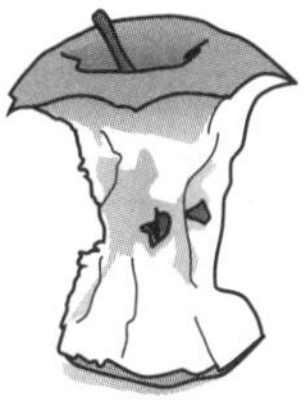

c ___

5.

st ___

6.

m ___

Read It Together Can you get a horn and a fork at a store?

Name ______________________________ Date ______________

Handwriting

High Frequency Words

Trace each word two times and then write it.

after after after

better better better

buy buy buy

idea idea idea

pull pull pull

until until until

Word Cards: *or, ore*

 horse	 porch	 shore	 storm
core	or	orange	form
forth	more	corn	sore
chore	born	horn	swore
explore	force	store	torch
tore	wore	north	sports
bore	snore	for	gore

High Frequency Word Cards

above	after
again	better
away	buy
change	idea
seven	pull
sometimes	until

Name ____________________ Date ____________

Venn Diagram

Compare Genres

Compare a history article and a blog entry.

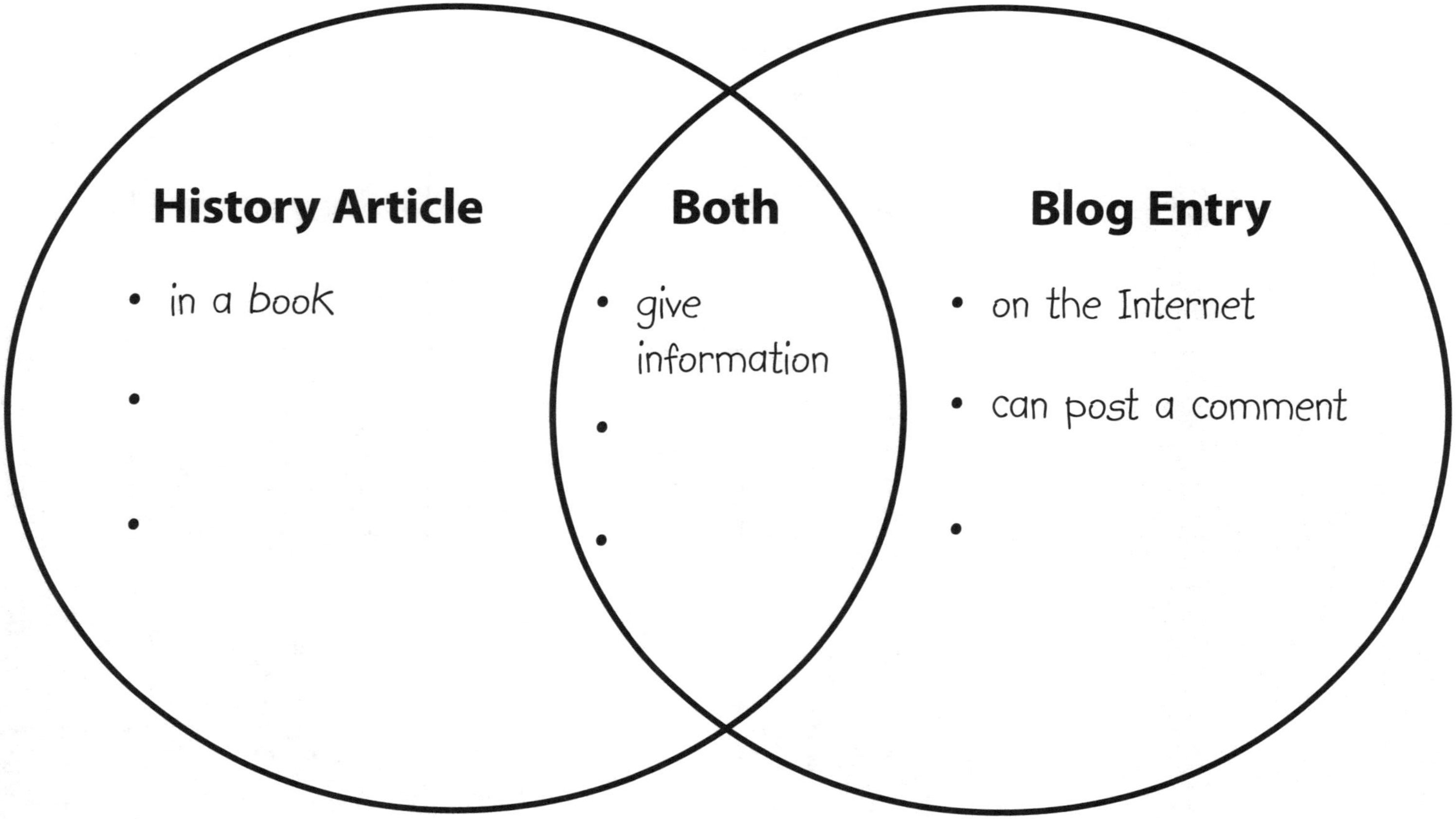

Take turns with a partner. Express your opinion about a history article and a blog entry.

Name ______________________ Date ____________

Phonics

Syllables

Draw a line between the syllables in each word. Circle the word that names the picture.

1.

darkroom

dolphin

dolly

2.

piglet

picnic

pillow

3.

pulley

pumpkin

puppy

4.

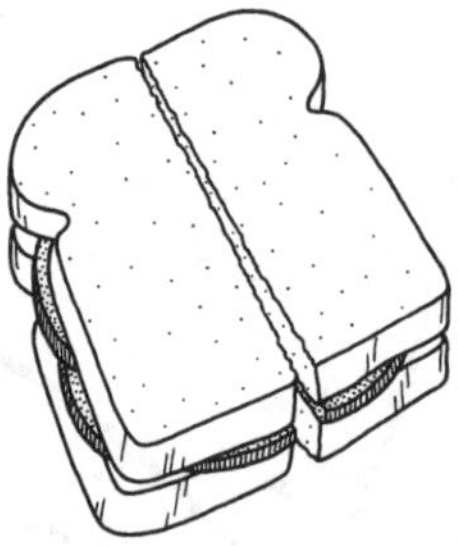

sandlot

sandbox

sandwich

5.

dentists

ducklings

disclose

6.

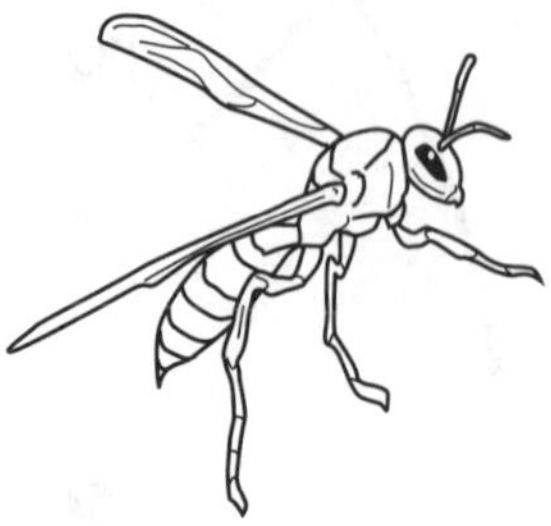

handbag

hornet

hilltop

7.

100

hundred

happy

happen

8.

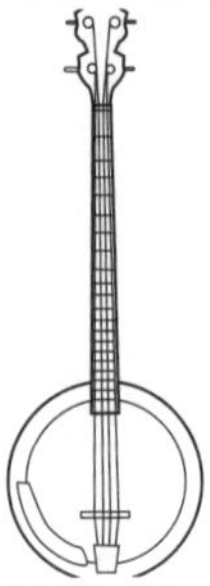

banjo

basket

baggage

Read It Together We have pumpkin muffins for our picnic.

Name ______________________ Date ____________

High Frequency Words

Let's Go Sledding!

Write a word from the box to complete each sentence.

High Frequency **Words**
after
better
buy
idea
pull
until

1. Mom wants to make a snowman ______________ the storm.

2. Tad has a better ______________ .

3. He wants to ______________ a sled at the store.

4. They ______________ the sled to a big hill.

5 Tad sleds ______________ lunchtime!

Name ______________________________ Date ______________

Grammar: Irregular Past Tense

Mix and Match Sentences

Play with a partner. One partner makes a choice from Column A, Column B, and Column C, and then says a sentence with the words. The other partner retells the sentence, using the past-tense form of the verb.

A	B	C
I	is	my ticket
you	have	first
he	has	on a plane
she	bring	to Florida
it	send	cold
we	go	excited
they	fly	in first grade
		with Mom and Dad
		three sisters
		a new computer
		a snack
		your friend
		a pillow for the trip
		to a new school
		to my seat
		last week
		an email message
		new friends
		a letter

Name ______________________ Date ____________

Phonics

Syllables

Read the words above each line. Draw a line to divide the syllables. Circle and write the word that completes the sentence.

classroom **muffin**

1. My ______________ is full of animal facts.

windows **children**

2. All the ______________ picked animals to study.

exclaim **ostrich**

3. I read that an ______________ can run very fast.

raccoon **traffic**

4. Jenny drew a ______________ with a mask.

rabbit **address**

5. Ann made a book of ______________ facts.

Name ______________________ Date ____________

Grammar & Writing

Write Irregular Past-Tense Verbs

Read the email. Then choose a word from the box that goes with the sentence. Write the word.

brought	flew	sent	was	had	went

Dear Jason,

We ______________ an awesome plane trip! Taking off was cool. First, the plane ______________ to the end of the runway. Then the engines roared, and the plane began to speed down the runway. Suddenly, it just lifted off the ground! A flight attendant ______________ me some juice in a plastic glass. He even gave me snacks. Before I knew it, it ______________ time to land. The plane ______________ so fast, we were not in the air for long at all! I ______________ you this email as soon as we landed.

Your friend,
Ramón

Name ______________________ Date ______________

Grammar: Regular Past Tense

Make It Past Tense

Grammar Rules Past-Tense Verbs

To make a verb about the past:

- Add *-ed* to the end of a regular verb, like *watch*.
- Use a special form of an irregular verb, like *fly*.

1. Play with a partner.

2. Spin the spinner.

3. Change the verb to the past tense.

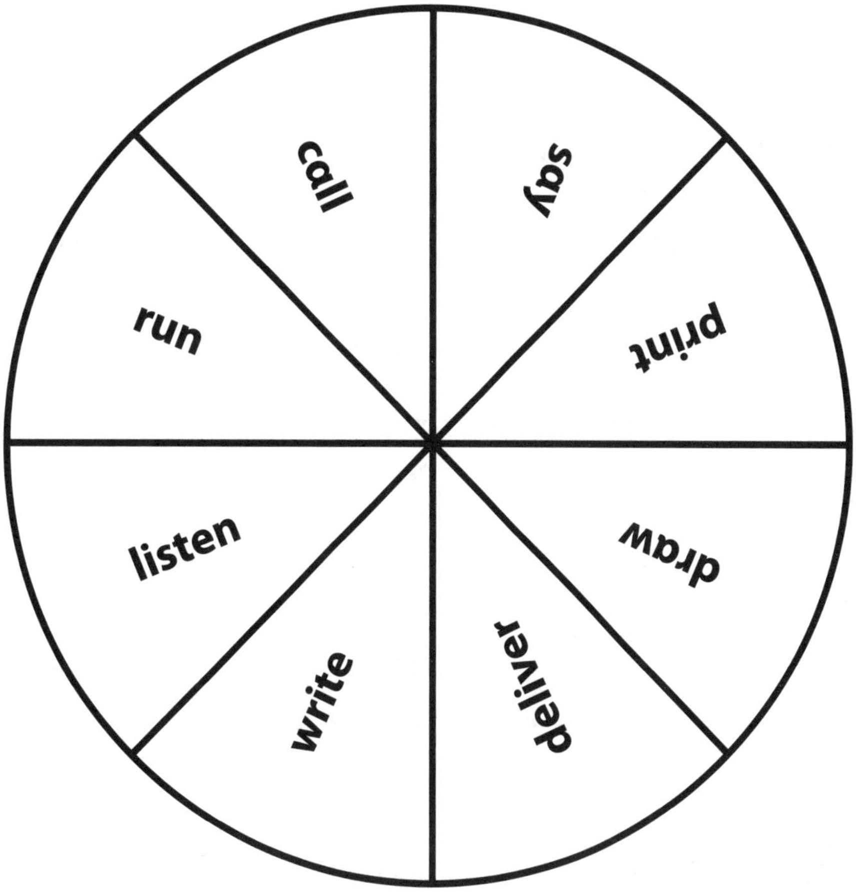

Make a Spinner

1. Put a paper clip in the center of the circle.
2. Hold one end of the paper clip with a pencil.
3. Spin the paper clip around the pencil.

Name ______________________ Date ____________

Phonics

Words with ir, er, ur

girl

fern

nurse

Circle the word that names each picture.

1.  shirt sheet sort	**2.** 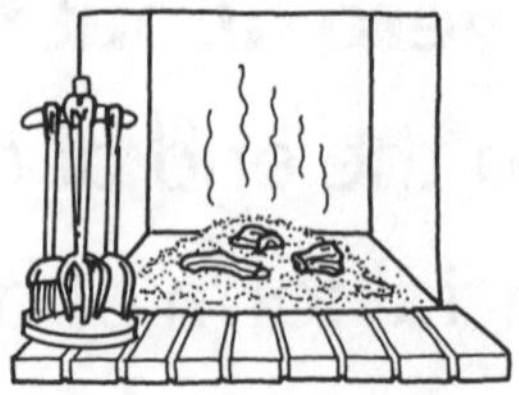 born barn burn
3.  core curl car	**4.**  thud third thorn
5.  clerk clock curb	**6.**  skit skirt skate
7.  fir far for	**8.**  purl perch purse

Read It Together The clerk sells a skirt, a shirt, and a purse.

Name ______________________ Date ____________

Character Description Chart

Describe Character's Feelings

List what Marta says or does. Then describe what this shows about how she feels.

Character	What the Character Says or Does	What This Shows About How the Character Feels
Marta		

Name ______________________ Date ____________

Phonics

Words with ir, er, ur

Circle the word that completes the sentence and write it.

curve first

1. Bert is my very ______________ dog.

jerk fur

2. He has black and white ______________ .

herd chirp

3. Bert helps us ______________ sheep.

turn verb

4. He makes the sheep ______________ turn.

whirls hurts

5. When he plays, he ______________ and twirls!

Name ______________________ Date ______________

Phonics

Syllables

Draw a line between the syllables in each word.
Circle the word that names the picture.

1.

giraffe

garden

garlic

2.

target

thirsty

teacher

3.

turban

turkey

turnip

4.

circus

carpool

corncob

5.

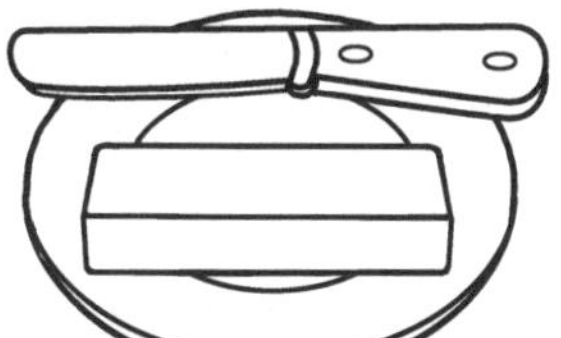

butter

birthday

burden

6.

servant

surprise

squirrel

7.

forty

farther

furry

8.

latter

lobster

letter

Read It Together Is a lobster or a squirrel furry?

Name ______________________ Date ____________

Handwriting

High Frequency Words

Trace each word two times and then write it.

also also also

call call call

fall fall fall

important important

important

story story story

tomorrow tomorrow

tomorrow

Word Cards: *ir, er, ur*

 bird	3 number	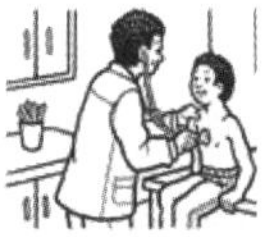 nurse	 skirt
Thursday	offer	birth	curl
girl	fur	curb	stir
her	perch	fern	panther
purse	winter	stern	whisper
hurt	alert	turn	thirst
third	curt	twirl	shirt

High Frequency Word Cards

been	also
down	call
hard	fall
now	important
number	story
push	tomorrow

Phonics

Endings -er, -est

With a partner, cut out the cards and shuffle them. Take turns picking a card and using the word in a sentence. Then sort the cards into piles. Repeat for all the cards.

high	big
higher	bigger
highest	biggest
close	funny
closer	funnier
closest	funniest

Name ____________________ Date ____________

High Frequency Words

Who Lives Here?

Write a word from the box to complete each sentence.

High Frequency Words
also
call
fall
important
story
tomorrow

1. This is my home. It's ____________ Kurt's home.

2. I live on the first ____________ .

3. People will move in ____________ .

4. We ____________ to ask if they need help.

5. It's ____________ to tell them that we are good helpers and will not let their boxes fall!

Name ______________________ Date ____________

Grammar: Expanding Sentences

Build Longer Sentences

because	before	after	because	before	after
because	before	after	because	before	after

We ate apples.	It rained.
I like this music.	They had gone to camp.
Jake went to the pool.	It was hungry.
The airplane flew to Boston.	It was very hot.
The bird watched the worm.	The movie started.
The mouse jumped.	You saw the movie.
Janet walked in the woods.	They are nice and crisp.
Ruff smelled like a skunk.	The sun shone brightly.
Dad cooked dinner.	It took off.
I visited my grandmother.	Mom told a funny joke.
My sister talked to her friend.	It is happy.
I put on my boots.	I threw a pillow at it.
Tracey wore her sunglasses.	He returned from the woods.
I laughed.	She called me on the phone.
You cried.	The ground was muddy.

Name ______________________ Date __________

Phonics

Endings -er, -est

long		+ er = longer	long		+ est = longest
late	– e	+ er = later	late	– e	+ est = latest
hot		+ t + er = hotter	hot		+ t + est = hottest
happy – y + i + er = happier			happy – y + i + est = happiest		

Add *-er* or *-est* to the word to complete the sentence and write it.

high

1. Bert's kite flies the ______________ of all the kites.

big

2. Ty's kite is ______________ than Kirk's kite.

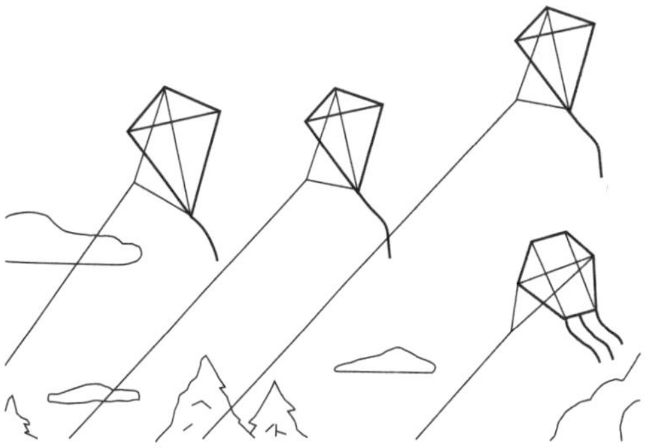

speedy

3. Kirk's kite is ______________ than Ty's kite.

nice

4. I like my kite. I think it is the ______________ of all!

Name ______________________ Date ____________

Grammar & Writing

Use Conjunctions

Read the story. Then choose a word from the box that goes with the sentence. You can use each word more than once.

because	before	after

Danny packed his suitcase before his family left for the airport.

"Take your book ____________ we will be at the airport a long time," said his mother.

Danny remembered something ____________ they left home. "I forgot to water my hamster."

Dad answered, "Don't worry ____________ Grandpa can give your hamster fresh water."

Name ______________________ Date ____________

Vocabulary

Picture It

1. Form pairs. Choose a pair to be the artists and a pair to be the guessers.
2. The artists secretly select a Key Word.
3. The artists draw a picture to show the word's meaning.
4. The guessers guess what Key Word the picture shows.
5. Switch roles.

record	music	better	tool	easier	new
old	invent	machine	build	modern	feel

1.	**2.**
3.	**4.**

Keeping Score

If the guessers answer correctly, they get 1 point.
The first pair to get 3 points wins!

Name ____________________ Date __________

Character Description Chart

A New Old Tune

List the things Max and Nell say or do. Then describe what this shows about how the character feels.

Character	What the Character Says or Does	What This Shows About How the Character Feels
Max	• Wow •	• He feels surprised. •
Nell	• •	• •

Use your chart to retell the story to a partner.

Name ______________________ Date ____________

Phonics

air, ear, are

airplane

pear

hare

Circle the word that names each picture.

1.  burr bar bear	**2.**  stairs stars stirs
3. 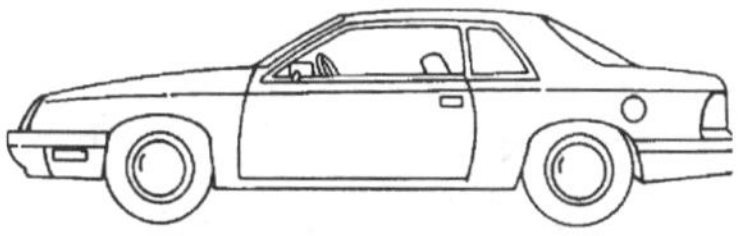 core care car	**4.**  her hair here
5.  may more mare	**6.**  pair par purr
7. 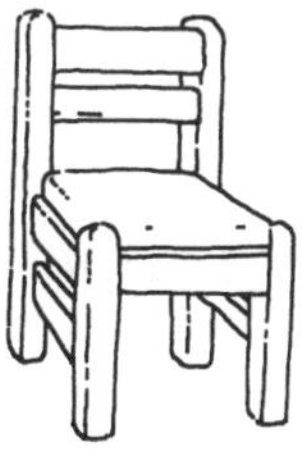 char chair chore	**8.**  score square spur

Read It Together Could you ride a hare or a mare?

Name ______________________ Date __________

Phonics

Words with air, ear, are

Read and trace each word. Write the word that completes each sentence.

share wear pair scare

1. Clare and Blair are a ______________ of twins.

2. They ______________ matching dresses.

3. They ______________ their lunches.

4. They ______________ a joke on Mom, too.

5. They yell, "Boo" and ______________ her!

Name ______________________ Date __________

Handwriting

High Frequency Words

Trace each word two times and then write it.

began began began

brother brother brother

enough enough enough

even even even

learn learn learn

second second second

Word Cards: *air, _ear, _are, eer, ear*

 bear	 square	 deer	 ear
care	gear	cheerful	chair
year	stair	spear	pear
sheer	share	airplane	dare
cheer	pair	hair	mare
steer	peer	fair	fear
wear	scare	near	hear

High Frequency Word Cards

children	began
her	brother
house	enough
school	even
thought	learn
word	second

Name ______________________ Date ______________

Venn Diagram

Compare Genres

Compare a story and poetry.

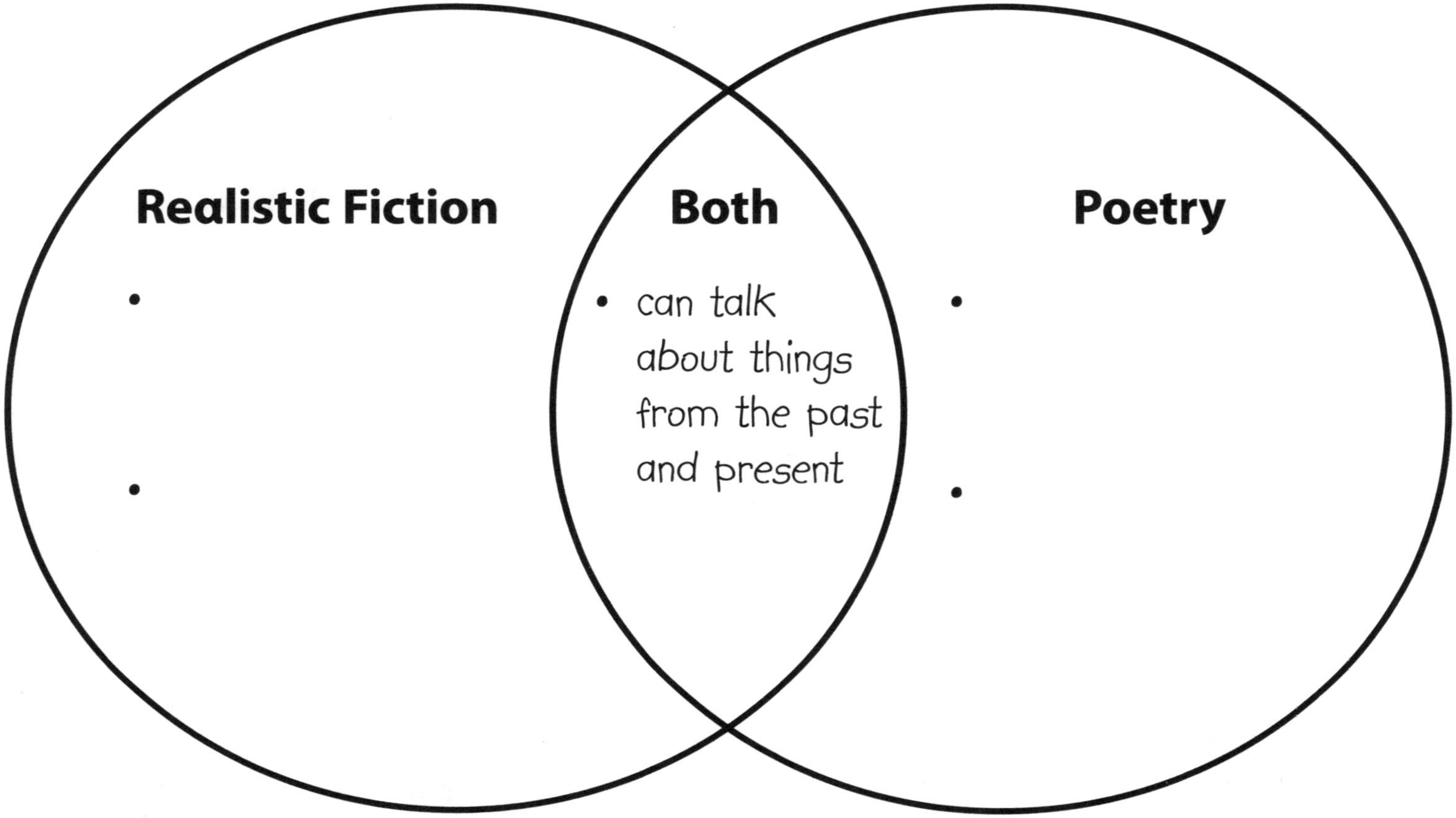

Take turns with a partner. Tell how a story and poetry are alike and different.

Name ____________________ Date ____________

Phonics

Words with eer, ear

Cut along the dotted lines. Write *d*, *p*, *st*, and *ch* in each box of one pull strip and *d*, *n*, *y*, and *g* in each box of the other. Put the strips through the slits with the arrows pointing up. Read the words you make.

deer

tear

____ eer

____ ear

Name ______________________ Date ____________

High Frequency Words

Learning to Ride

Write a word from the box to complete each sentence.

High Frequency **Words**
began
brother
enough
even
learn
second

1. Mom is teaching my ______________ to ride.

2. How well does Victor ______________ ?

3. He tries hard ______________ , so he learns well!

4. He just ______________ today.

5. He can ride for a few seconds ______________ if Mom lets go!

Name ____________________ Date ____________

Grammar: Future Tense

Use the Future Tense

1. You play on the white squares; your partner plays on the shaded squares.
2. Place a marker on a word on a white square.
3. Say a sentence about the future using *will* or *going to*.
4. Your partner places a marker on a word on a shaded square and says a sentence about the future using the other form of the future tense.
5. Keep playing until you use all the words on your color square. Then change colors.

hurry	hug	carry	fly
drag	play	want	talk
open	answer	stop	pull

Name ______________________ Date __________

Phonics

Words with eer, ear

Circle the word that completes the sentence and write it.

year **sneer**

1. Rose got a bike this ______________.

beards **gears**

2. It has three ______________.

ears **steers**

3. It has a bell to ring while she ______________.

deer **tear**

4. Look! There is a ______________!

cheer **hear**

5. Rose rings her bell for it to ______________.

Name ______________________________ Date ______________

Grammar & Writing

Write in the Future

Read the story. Then choose a word or words from the box that goes with the sentence.

we're going to	am going to	I'll	we'll	it'll	she's going to

I love reading about the past. My class is starting a history unit. We're going to learn about how people used to live. I ______________ talk to my great-grandmother. She likes to tell me about when she was a little girl. Then ______________ report to the class. ______________ make a scrapbook of people's memories about the past. ______________ be really interesting to read the scrapbook. Maybe I can show it to my great-grandmother. ______________ love our scrapbook with her memories in it!

Name ______________________ Date ____________

Grammar: Future-Tense Verbs

Make It Happen

Grammar Rules Future-Tense Verbs

To make a verb tell about the future, add *will, am going to, is going to,* or *are going to* before the verb.

You will listen to music. He is going to read a book.

1. **Play with a partner.**
2. **Choose one word from the Future column and one word from the Verb column below. Create as many sentences as you can.**
3. **Cross out the words you choose.**
4. **Your partner takes a turn.**
5. **The player who writes more complete sentences wins.**

Future	Verb
will	build
am going to	invent
is going to	make
are going to	write
will	draw

Name ______________________ Date ____________

Prewrite Graphic Organizer: Main Idea and Details Diagram

Main Idea and Details Diagram

Main Idea

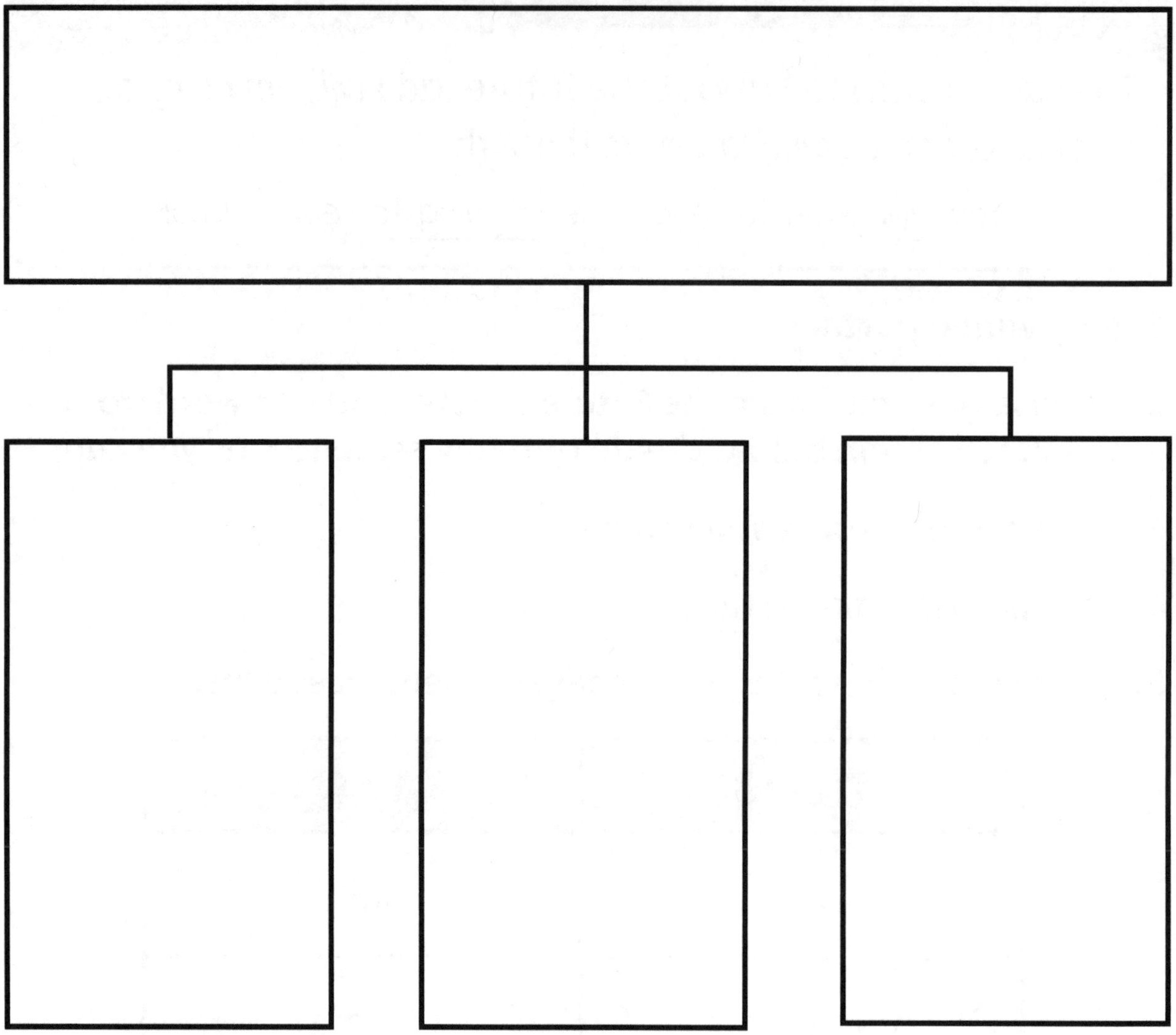

Detail **Detail** **Detail**

Organization Checklist

✓ Did you write the main idea at the beginning?
✓ Do details tell more about the main idea?
✓ Do your ideas flow nicely from one idea to the next idea?

Name ______________________ Date ____________

Phonics

Words with al, all

salt

ball

Circle the word that names each picture.

1.

tall

tea

till

2.

bowled

bad

bald

3.

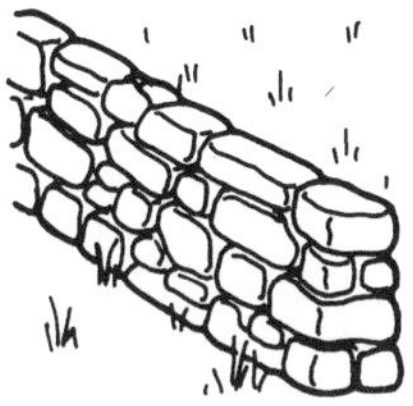

wheel

wall

whale

4.

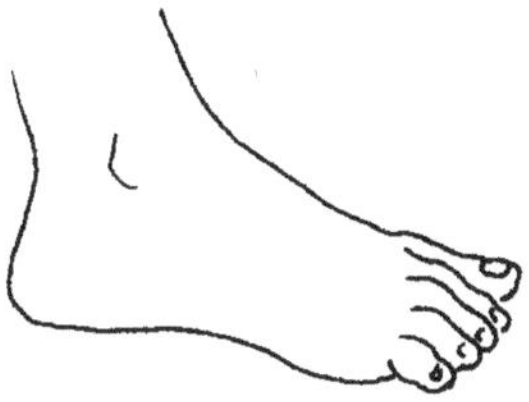

heel

hall

hail

5.

fail

feel

fall

6.

halt

hate

heat

7.

mail

mall

meal

8.

smile

small

smell

Read It Together The tall man halts by the small wall.

Name ______________________ Date ______________

T-Chart

Use Information

Draw symbols and signs that you see in town. Then write what they mean in the column on the right.

Signs and Symbols	What It Means

Name ____________________ Date ____________

Phonics

Words with al, all

Complete the word so it names the picture.

1.

fall

2.

s t

3.

c

4.

st

5.

baseb

6.

t est

Read It Together What kind of ball do you play in the fall?

Name ______________________ Date ______________

Handwriting

High Frequency Words

Trace each word two times and then write it.

about about about

below below below

between between

mountain mountain

water water water

world world world

Word Cards: *al, all*

 salt	 ball	 wallet	 palm
call	wall	hall	bald
talc	fall	waltz	malt
squall	false	always	halt
baseball	scald	also	mall
calm	fallen	overall	stall
almost	tall	balm	small

Spelling & Word Work

High Frequency Word Cards

before	about
could	below
people	between
today	mountain
warm	water
were	world

Phonics

Endings -es, -ed, -ing

Cut out the cards with a partner. Shuffle them and find matches. Read and act out the words.

hum	hums
hummed	humming
cry	cries
cried	crying
smile	smiles
smiled	smiling

Name ______________________ Date ____________

High Frequency Words

Down in the Valley

Write a word from the box to complete each sentence.

High Frequency **Words**
about
below
between
mountain
water
world

1. A valley is ______________ two mountains.

2. Horses drink ______________ from the stream.

3. We look down to see the horses ______________.

4. From up high, the horses look like the smallest ______________ horses in the ______________.

5. They are really ______________ the same size as other horses.

Name ______________________________ Date ______________

Grammar: Writing a Letter

Write a Letter

Read the words in the box. Then rewrite them in the right order to make a letter. Use only the parts that are correct.

I hope you can come see me play.

Thank you for the map game.

dear Grandpa

love, Lauren

I will play with it every day.

Dear Grandpa,

Love, Lauren

Name ______________________________ Date ____________

Phonics

Short -es, -ed, -ing

Circle the word that completes the sentence and write it.

throwing **pitches**

1. Margie ____________ the ball.

hoping **planned**

2. Beth is ____________ to hit the ball.

trying **batted**

3. When Beth ____________ last inning, she struck out.

tries **swinging**

4. Now she ____________ again and hits the ball.

jogged **running**

5. Beth is ____________ to first base.

Name ______________________ Date ____________

Grammar and Writing

Use Capital Letters in Letters

Read the letter. Then choose a word from the box to complete the sentences.

Lake Michigan	Chicago	Dear	Love	day	Monday

Dear
______________ Aunt Lucy,

Hello from the city of ______________ . Our trip is a lot of fun. One ______________ we went to the zoo. Yesterday morning, we went on a boat on ______________ . We will come home on ______________ .

______________ ,

Reiko

Name ______________________ Date ____________

Vocabulary

Around the World

1. The traveler stands behind a challenger.
2. Listen to the clue. Find the Key Word and say it.
3. The first to answer correctly travels to the next student on the right. The first traveler to go all around the circle wins.

map	key	meaning	symbol	picture	useful

CLUES

- A ______________ can be a shape or picture.
- A ______________ tells the meaning of a map's symbols.
- A map is ______________ for finding places.
- He drew a ______________ of a house.
- Look on the ______________ to find the library.
- A key shows the ______________ of a symbol or sign.

Name ______________________ Date ____________

T-Chart

If Maps Could Talk

Draw symbols and signs from "If Maps Could Talk." Write their meanings in the column on the right.

Signs and Symbols	What It Means
	• mostly sunny
	•
	•

Take turns with a partner. Tell what you learned about signs, symbols, and maps from the text.

Name ______________________________ Date ______________

Phonics

Words with oi, oy

Cut along the dotted lines. Write *b, c, s,* and *sp* on one pull strip and *b, j, s,* and *t* on the other. Put the strips through the slits with the arrows pointing up. Read the words you make.

oil

boy

oil

oy

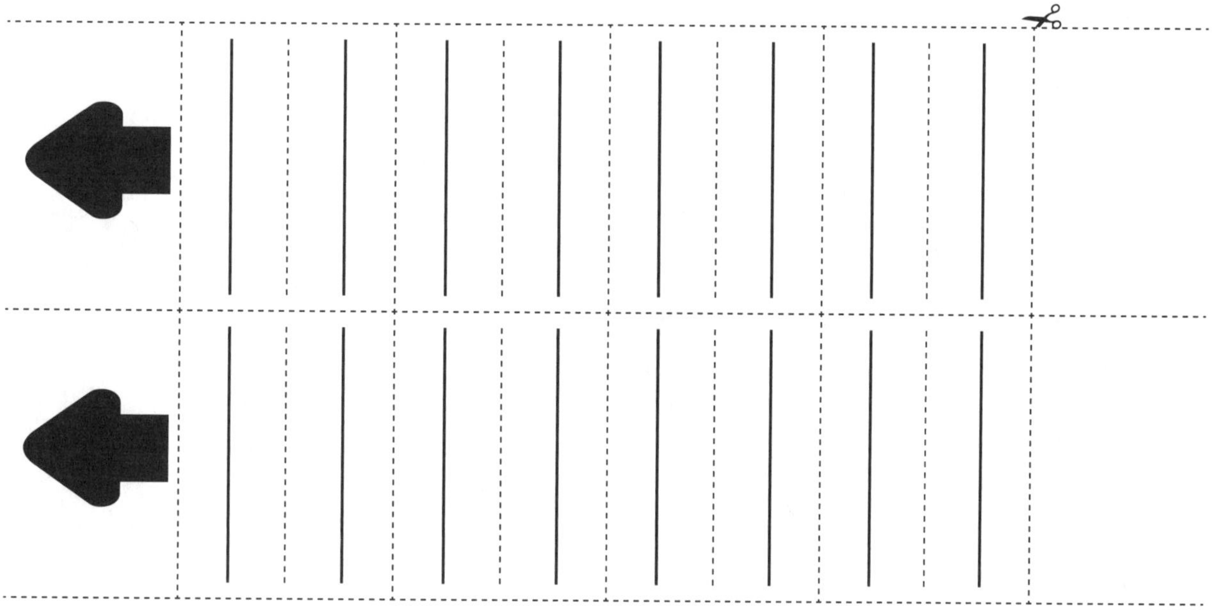

Name ______________________________ Date ____________

Phonics

Words with oi, oy

Complete each word so it names the picture.

1.

boy

2.

t

3.

b l

4.

c n

5.

n se

6.

p nt

Read It Together The boy's toy makes a lot of noise!

Name ______________________ Date ________

Handwriting

High Frequency Words

Trace each word two times and then write it.

another another another

begin begin begin

done done done

follow follow follow

our our our

should should should

Spelling & Word Work

Word Cards: *oi, oy, ou, ow*

 point	 boy	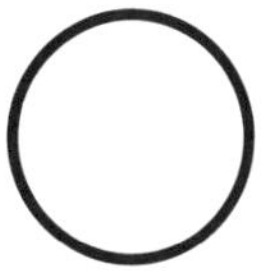 round	 cow
choice	South	oil	destroy
spoil	howl	boil	crown
enjoy	mouse	soy	cloud
out	voice	loud	royal
down	growl	crowd	toy
shout	joy	noise	frown

Spelling & Word Work

High Frequency Word Cards

after	another
better	begin
buy	done
idea	follow
pull	our
until	should

Name ________________________ Date ____________

T-Chart

Compare Genres

Compare an informational text and a poem.

Informational Text	Poem
gives definitions	uses words to create images in your mind

Take turns with a partner. Ask questions about an informational text and a poem.

Name ______________________________ Date ______________

Phonics

Words with <u>ou</u>, <u>ow</u>

Cut out the picture cartds. Paste each picture card under the word with the same spelling for /ow/.

mouse

cow

house

frown

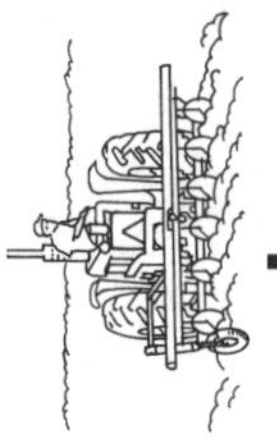

plow

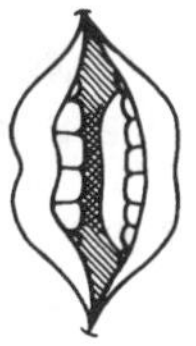

mouth

owl

hound

Name ______________________ Date ____________

High Frequency Words

Hansel and Gretel

Write a word from the box to complete each sentence.

High Frequency **Words**
another
begin
done
follow
our
should

1. Hansel and Gretel ______________ their walk.

2. "We should drop bread crumbs to mark ______________ way," they say.

3. "We can ______________ the crumbs home."

4. Birds eat one crumb and then ______________ .

5. When the birds are ______________ , the children still find their way home!

Grammar: Adverbs

Word Cards: Adverbs

quickly	often	there	always
later	soon	slowly	never
here	carefully	sometimes	now
run	eat	put	read
talk	see	sit	call
play	sing	walk	stand

Name ______________________ Date ____________

Phonics

Words with ou, ow

Complete each word so it names the picture.

1.

cloud

2.

c

3.

fr n

4.

m se

5.

h se

6.

pl

Read It Together I frown if I see a mouse in my house.

Name ________________________ Date ____________

Grammar and Writing

Write with Adverbs

Read the story. Then choose a word from the box that best completes the sentences.

always	carefully	later	loudly	never	soon

Sam looked outside. He ___always___ looks out his window when he wakes up. Everything was covered with ice! "Ice storm!" he said ______________ "I have ______________ seen such thick ice." Sam stepped ___carefully___ out the front door. It was so slippery he almost fell down! "I hope the sun comes out and melts the ice ______________!" Sam cried. "I think I will take my walk ______________."

Name ______________________ Date ______________

Grammar: Adverbs

Trip to the Train Station

Grammar Rules Adverbs

Adverbs can tell:

- **how** something happens.
- **where** something happens.
- **when** something happens.

Read the passage. Categorize the underlined adverbs in the chart below.

My grandfather and I walked quickly to the train station. We turned left at the corner. Then we turned right on Park Street. We waited patiently for the train. The train will arrive soon.

Adverbs		
Where	**How**	**When**
	quickly	

With a partner, add more adverbs to the chart. Use one of the adverbs in a sentence.

Name ______________________________ Date ______________

Phonics

Suffixes -ful, -less

thoughtless

thoughtful

Circle the word that names the picture.

1.

hopeless
hopeful
helpless

2.

germless
graceless
graceful

3.

funnel
fearless
fearful

4.

helpless
harmless
helpful

5.

cheerful
careful
careless

6.

useless
using
useful

7.

peaceful
painless
playful

8.

spotless
spotted
skillful

Read It Together Is it helpful to have a playful puppy in a spotless room?

Name ______________________________ Date ______________

Phonics

Suffixes -er, -ly

skat**er**

proud**ly**

Circle the word that names the picture.

1.

farmer
firmly
faster

2.

leaper
larger
loudly

3.

quirky
quickly
quilter

4.

tiger
tenderly
teacher

5.

painter
painfully
pepper

6.

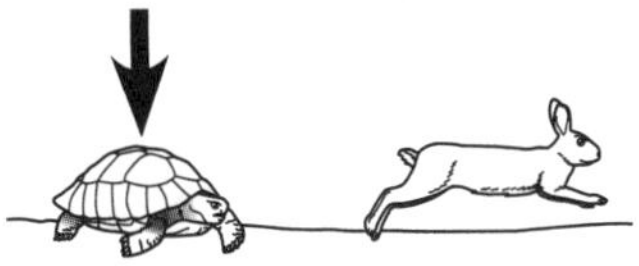

sharply
slowly
sleeper

7.

swimmer
softly
smartly

8.

singer
simply
suddenly

Read It Together The farmer talks softly but snores loudly.

Name ______________________________ Date ______________

Problem-and-Solution Chart

Identify Problem and Solution

Tell a different story about Jack. Imagine Jack is with a friend. Complete the Problem-and-Solution Chart.

Problem:

Event 1:

Event 2:

Solution:

Name ______________________________ Date ______________

Phonics

Suffixes -ful, -less

Circle the word that completes the sentence and write it.

tearful **cloudless**

1. Phil is driving on a hot, ______________ day.

endless **skillful**

2. The trip is long and seems to be ______________.

cheerful **priceless**

3. Phil was ______________ when they started.

graceful **hopeless**

4. Now he is starting to feel ______________.

pointless **thankful**

5. He will be ______________ when they stop.

Name ______________________ Date ____________

Phonics

Suffixes -er, -ly

Circle the word that completes the sentence and write it.

loudly **runner**

1. Rosa is a really good ______________.

talker **quickly**

2. She races ______________ around the track.

leader **nicely**

3. Right now, the ______________ in this race is Anna.

thinker **closely**

4. Rosa is following Anna very ______________.

winners **safety**

5. I think there might be two ______________ in this race!

Name ______________________ Date ____________

Handwriting

High Frequency Words

Trace each word two times and then write it.

country country country

earth earth earth

family family family

friend friend friend

paper paper paper

picture picture picture

Spelling & Word Work

Word Cards: *-ful, -less, -er, un-, re-*

 singer	 talker	 teacher	 helpful
reread	hopeful	unpack	playful
careful	careless	unbutton	unlock
thankful	harmless	skillful	reopen
homeless	fearless	driver	clueless
retell	untie	player	reheat
hopeless	unzip	retie	worker

High Frequency Word Cards

also	country
call	earth
fall	family
important	friend
story	paper
tomorrow	picture

Name ______________________ Date ____________

Phonics

Prefixes un-, re-

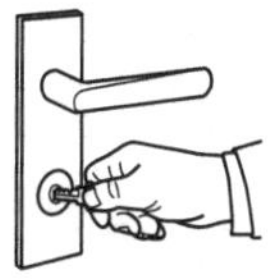

unlock

rewrite

Circle the word that names each picture.

1. 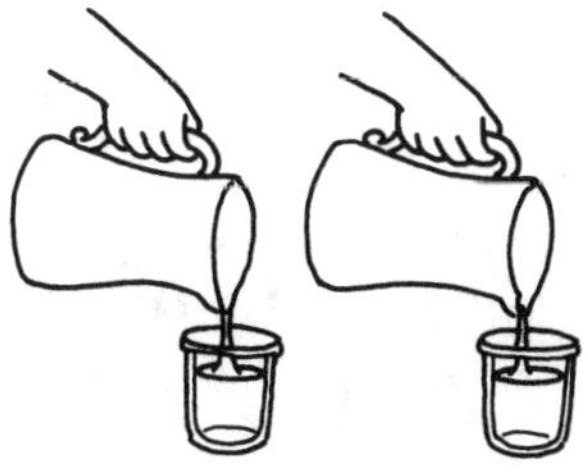
   - unfilled
   - refilled
   - unlock

2. 
   - reheat
   - undo
   - unhappy

3. 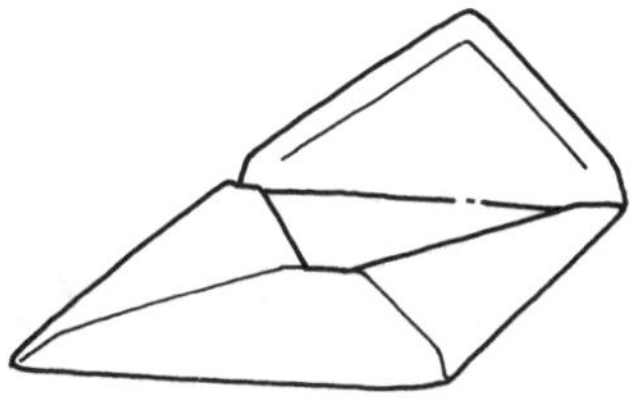
   - resealed
   - unsealed
   - remake

4. 
   - replace
   - unkind
   - rewind

5. 

   - unlike
   - unsafe
   - reset

6. 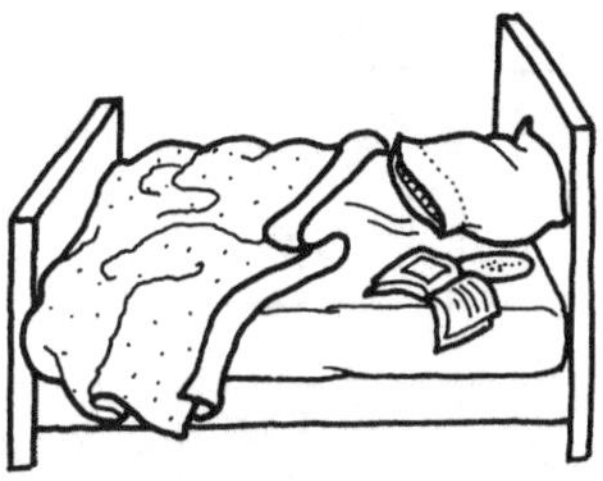
   - reopen
   - unmade
   - unfair

7. 
   - untied
   - retied
   - recharge

8. 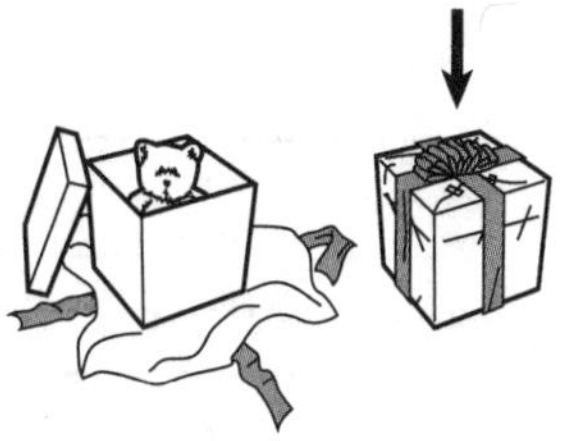
   - unwrapped
   - rewrapped
   - recalled

Read It Together I untied the ribbon, replaced it, and rewrapped the gift.

Name ______________________ Date ____________

High Frequency Words

The Other Side of the Earth

Write a word from the box to complete each sentence.

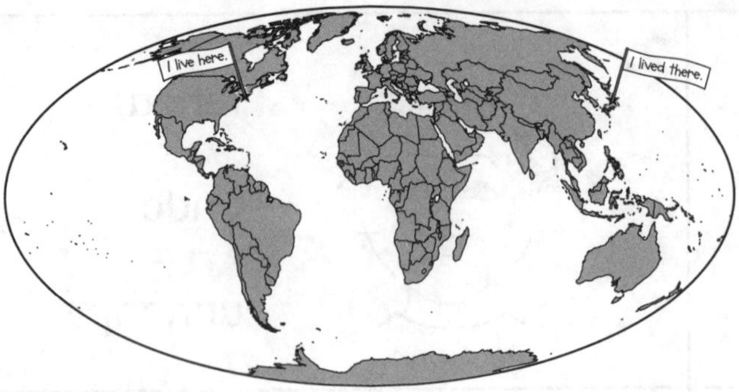

High Frequency Words
country
earth
family
friend
paper
picture

1. My family moved to this ______________ last year.

2. Before that, we lived on the other side of the ______________.

3. Would you hand me that piece of ______________?

4. It shows a ______________ of my old home.

5. The girl in it is my best ______________.

Name ____________________ Date ____________

Grammar: Punctuation

Word Cards: Punctuation

.	!	?
rabbit	swim	blue
big	fast	hot
run	eat	want
Mark	map	lost
city	market	buy
read	Sarah	watch

Name ______________________ Date ____________

Phonics

Prefixes un-, re-

Circle the word that completes each sentence and write it.

untied **replayed**

1. Carlos's boots were ______________________ , so he had to tie them.

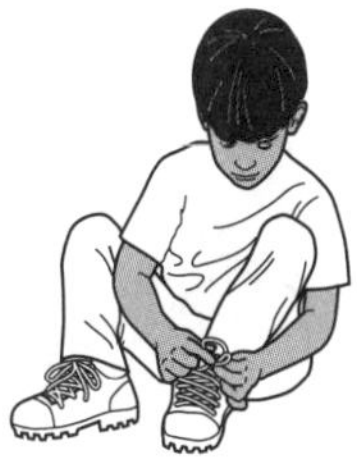

unlike **recall**

2. He couldn't ______________________ where he put his jacket, so he had to find it. Then he went out.

remake **unlucky**

3. It was raining! Carlos felt so ______________________ .

reread **unzipped**

4. Carlos ______________________ his jacket.

reheated **unhooked**

5. His mom ______________________ soup for lunch.

Name ______________________________ Date ______________

Grammar and Writing

Use Commas and End Marks

Read the story. Then choose punctuation marks from the box that correctly complete each sentence.

,	,	.	.	!	?

The date was May 3 __,__ 2012. Will was on a hike. He looked up in a tree ____ The tree was tall, green ____ and leafy. It was hard to see through the leaves ____ Can you guess what he saw ____ He saw a flash of red. It was the biggest woodpecker Will had ever seen ____

Name ______________________ Date ____________

Vocabulary

Picture It

1. Form pairs. Choose a pair to be the artists and a pair to be the guessers.
2. The artists secretly select a Key Word.
3. The artists draw a picture to show the word's meaning
4. The guessers guess what Key Word the picture shows.
5. Switch roles.

path	north	south	east	west	near
left	right	location	direction	far	follow

1.	2.
3.	4.

Keeping Score

If the guessers answer correctly, they get 1 point.

The first pair to get 3 points wins!

Name ______________________ Date ______________

Problem-and-Solution Chart

Caperucita Roja

List the events and solution to the problem below.

Problem: Big Bad Wolf is trying to eat Abuelita.

Event 1:

Event 2:

Event 3:

Solution:

Use your Problem-and-Solution Chart to retell the story to a partner.

Name ______________________ Date ____________

Phonics

Words with -le

apple

Circle the word that names the picture.

1. 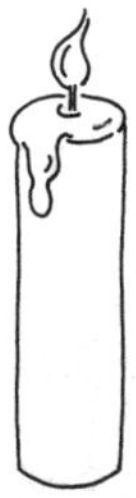 candle / crackle / kettle	**2.**  pretzel / paddle / puzzle
3.  bundle / bottle / bubble	**4.**  cancel / cuddle / cattle
5.  puddle / pickle / purple	**6.** 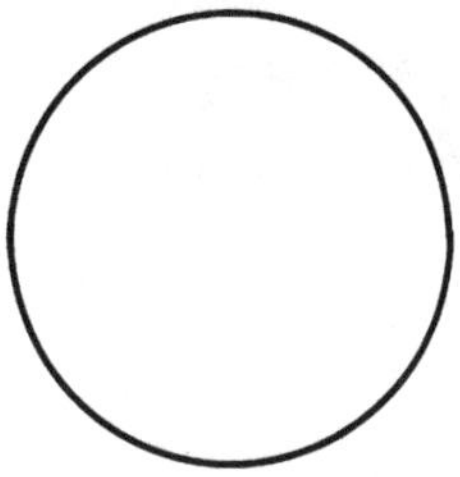 settle / circle / saddle
7.  tickle / tunnel / turtle	**8.**  ruffle / rattle / rubble

Read It Together Do turtles or cattle have shells?

Name ______________________ Date ______________

Phonics

Words with -le

Complete each word so it names the picture.

1.

bubbles

2.

sadd___

3.

bunn___

4.

kett___

5.

pebb___s

6.

cand___

Read It Together Do you put a saddle or a kettle on the stove?

Name ______________________ Date __________

Handwriting

High Frequency Words

Trace each word two times and then write it.

along along along

answer answer answer

city city city

often often often

something something

yellow yellow yellow

Spelling & Word Work

Word Cards: Final Syllable C + *-le*, VCV Syllables

 apple	 table	 turtle	 cabin
bottle	visit	pilot	poodle
travel	needle	bacon	trouble
lemon	spider	tiger	circle
purple	broken	robin	motor
gentle	music	puddle	paper
wagon	battle	salad	puzzle

Spelling & Word Work

High Frequency Word Cards

began	along
brother	answer
enough	city
even	often
learn	something
second	yellow

Name ____________________ Date ____________

T-Chart

Compare Genres

Compare a fairy tale and a how-to article.

Fairy Tale	How-to Article
tells a story that cannot happen in real life	tells how to make something that is real

Take turns with a partner. Tell how a fairy tale and a how-to article are different.

Name ______________________ Date ____________

Phonics

Syllable Division

Draw a line to divide the syllables in each word. Write the words under the word divided the same way.

open	cabin	shadow
music	robot	river

spider	**wagon**
1. ______	4. ______
2. ______	5. ______
3. ______	6. ______

Name ______________________ Date ____________

High Frequency Words

What Do I See?

Write a word from the box to complete each sentence.

High Frequency **Words**
along
answer
city
often
something
yellow

1. Megan sees something ______________ in the sky. What is it?

2. Jacob gives the ______________. It is the sun.

3. Jacob sees something yellow ______________ the pond. What is it?

4. Megan knows. She ______________ sees it, too.

5. They see it here by the pond in the ______________ park. It is a duck!

Name ______________________________ Date ______________

Grammar: Prepositions

Use Prepositions

Read the preposition on the left side. Then draw a line to connect the preposition to the correct sentence on the right side.

1. on	We will meet __________ one o'clock.
2. from	I will be waiting __________ the big red roof.
3. at	Turn left and walk __________ the oak tree.
4. during	The park is __________ Main Street.
5. under	Walk __________ the park through the gate.
6. into	The geese fly all the way __________ Canada!
7. toward	The park is cool __________ the hot part of the day.

Name ______________________ Date ____________

Phonics

Syllable Division

Draw a line to divide each word into syllables.
Circle and write the word that completes the sentence.

travel **bagels**

1. I eat ______________ and cream cheese in the morning.

melon **pilot**

2. I have a piece of ______________, too.

salad **cabin**

3. For lunch, I like to eat a garden ______________.

frozen **cider**

4. I often drink apple ______________ at lunch, too.

never **bacon**

5. The best supper is ______________ burgers with a glass of cold milk.

Name ______________________________ Date ______________

Grammar and Writing

Write with Prepositions

Read the story. Then choose a word from the box that correctly completes each sentence.

at	around	between	during	on	toward

Mom and I took a walk ______on______ Saturday. We walked ______________ our neighborhood. First, we walked ______________ the park. The park is ______________ the river and the school. We stopped for lunch ______________ 12:30. The sun was shining ______________ our walk.

Name ______________________ Date ____________

Grammar: Prepositions

The Preposition Game

Grammar Rules Prepositions

Prepositions can tell where. Put prepositions before a noun that names a place.	*The book is on the table.*

next to	across	between	under
at			down
BEGIN			in
END			over
into	on	above	up

1. Play with a partner.
2. Use a small object for a game piece.
3. Flip a coin.

    = Move 1 space.

    = Move 2 spaces.
4. Use the preposition in a sentence.
5. Write the prepositional phrase on another sheet of paper.
6. The first one to the END wins!

Name ____________________ Date __________

Prewrite Graphic Organizer: Opinion-Reasons Chart

Opinion-Reasons Chart

Opinion

Reason **Reason** **Reason**

Fluency Checklist

✓ Did you name the story?
✓ Do your sentences flow smoothly from problem to solution?
✓ Did you give your opinion with reasons for it?
✓ Did you write in complete sentences?
✓ Does your writing sound natural?